The

Ocotillo

Review

Volume 7.2

Summer 2023

The Ocotillo Review Volume 7.2
©2023 Kallisto Gaia Press Inc.
All Rights Reserved

Attention Schools and businesses: For discounted prices on large orders please contact the publisher directly.

Kallisto Gaia Press Inc.
1801 E. 51st Street
Suite 365-246
Austin TX 78723
info@kallistogaiapress.org

Cover Design: Tony Burnett
Front Cover Painting: *Untitled* 16"X20" oil on canvas
    by Preston Burnett
Edited by Tony Burnett & Mary Day Long

ISSN: 2573-4113
ISBN: 978-1-952224-34-8

The Ocotillo Review

Volume 7.2

Summer 2023
New Horizons

FICTION - POETRY - TRUTH

Table of Contents
Poetry

Fiction

Truth

Contributors
166

Editorial Board

Precious Reader,

In the past I've mentioned how it's common for each issue of The Ocotillo Review to organically develop thematically. It's the reason we no longer request submissions on a particular theme. There's joy in seeing your words and ideas coalesce into an unexpected but prevalent idea. We are subtitling this issue "New Horizons". Although many of the poems, essays, and stories do revolve around a character embarking on a new beginning, the real reason for the subtitle references what is happening in the structure and leadership of The Ocotillo Review and Kallisto Gaia Press. I'm stepping down as the Executive Director. We founded our nonprofit literary adventure eight years ago with a modest Kickstarter campaign that earned out 12 minutes before the deadline and that has been our modus operandi for the duration of the publication. We've never been known for our quick response. In the words of the legendary Willie Dixon, "I'm built for comfort, I ain't built for speed". I haven't been in a hurry since 1986. I don't know if that will change with the new leadership, but I do know the torch is being passed to capable hands.

Our new Executive Director, Mary Day Long, has been with the organization since our third edition. She has served as our Nonfiction Editor, served on the board of directors, and shuttled two of our most successful single authors works from conception to publication. Her editorial talents, photography, and cover design are prevalent throughout our catalog.

Our next edition will feature a new poetry editor as well. Carole Mertz has served as an associate editor for several years as well as reading and scoring with our poetry contest teams and writing phenomenal critiques for our Critique Service.

It's my understanding that The Julia Darling Memorial Poetry Prize and the Chester B. Himes Memorial Short Fiction Prize will return in 2024. Keep your eyes open for other developments. We still have at least 6 single-author books releasing in the Spring and Summer of 2024 including at least two full-length novels! I'll have a hand in those. I will be shuffling through the hallowed halls of KGP until I'm dragged away kicking and screaming. Unfortunately, my Parkinson's has progressed to the point that I'm no longer able to maintain a 50-hour work week.

Plus, I have some writing to do. All the 4 & 5-star reviews I received for Watermelon Tattoo encouraged me to polish and shop my next novel, Mirage, about a psychopathic sheriff's deputy who pledges to single-handedly shut down a cartel-backed human smuggling operation responsible for the death of her childhood friend.

Thank you for letting our project into your life. I have experienced great joy in sharing the work of the poets and writers we have published. I hope it has given you inspiration and entertainment.

Unfortunately, I'm leaving the coffers a bit light. If you could make a tax-deductible donation at our website to help Mary keep the lights on and the writers paid, I would be sincerely grateful. Just consider it my going away present. I hope to see you out there in the writing community.

Before I get too emotional, I want to wish you a productive and fulfilling life. Don't hesitate to stay in touch.

Peace,

- Tony

Vainglory

I lose myself
in the empty branches of rage,
scatter myself across skin
that is spread thin,
like plastic on the mouth of a jar.
I dig down into the warmth
of stomach,
of heart.
Scorch fingertips
on a beckoning stove.
The blood between my legs
a horror, an intense
glowing reminder
that I am unsure as girl,
unsure as woman.
That wrath brimming.
The loss of sleepovers,
virtue.
The mourning over a grave
that reads, "I am everything."
The pillow fights,
the popcorn,
the flash of color that ended
child-like wonder.
Crimson licks the sky.
My cheeks flush.
When we are born,
who names us?
When we are born,
who carries us?

- **Sarah Weglarz**

Juanita's Marigolds

See those shorter strands of wire Miguel looped
through the links reconnecting the back fence
where it sagged from the metal frame he built
years ago to protect a large plot
of ground he plowed and planted each spring
with pintos, poblanos and potatoes
bordered by Juanita's marigolds?

Most evenings Miguel wound down after long days
on lawns and gardens in gated north side
communities weeding ornamental
displays and trimming manicured grasses,
back in his own yard for a brief twilit hour
tending his steadily ripening crops,
some special attention for marigolds.

- Milton Jordan

Faker

I had a little trick to keep
the rest of you from knowing—
when I reached the end of the food line,
I'd lean in and pretend to pay,
as I told the cafeteria lady my name,
so she could check it on the free lunch list—
this is how I learned to be an illusionist.

-Douglas Cole

Maria and Gabriel

The train station was crowded with tourists and early Christmas shoppers. The air was crisp and cool. He took a breath and told himself to calm down. It wasn't as if he hadn't practiced this until it was perfect in his mind. Still, some doubt lingered that would not let go. X had told him it was perfectly natural to have doubts, that he didn't stop being human. He remembered X looking him in the eye and asking him if he was sure he was ready. He had answered by flashing a broad grin. X had hugged him and whispered that he wished he had had a son like him. That made him happy.

He checked his watch and tightened his grip on the black leather case in his other hand. Still ten minutes until the express was due. He walked to a bench and sat down, carefully placing the bag between his legs. A young woman sat down on the next bench. Out of the corner of his eye he could see that she was attractive. Women still made him feel nervous and panicky. X had told him that the sexual power of modern women was one of the causes of male unhappiness. That the order of things had been reversed. "A man who lets a woman control him is not a proper man." It had occurred to him more than once that he had never seen X with a woman. He assumed that he was married and that his wife stayed at home, as she was supposed to. And yet...he felt that old pang of regret that he had never been with a woman. Once, Z had taken him to a strip club and he had been so excited watching the dancers that he thought he might faint. The next day Z went on a mission and never returned.

He looked at his watch. Five minutes to go. The woman took out a paperback book and started to read. X had said that fiction was an opiate that weakened the will to act. The woman read very rapidly, flipping the pages almost angrily. There was a slight smile on her mouth that made little dimples in her cheeks. She looked up suddenly and he had to turn away. Two minutes. His palms were sweating, his heart pounding. He tried to swallow but his mouth was too dry and he almost choked. The woman stared at him and asked if he was alright. He blushed scarlet and mumbled that he just swallowed wrong. She laughed and said that it had happened to her. He felt both warm and very cold. One minute. People were picking up their bags and Christmas presents and approaching the track. Fifteen seconds. He should also be getting up but somehow couldn't move. The woman put the book back in her bag, reached out a gloved hand and said her name was Maria. "Are you taking this train?" Ten seconds. He could hear the train now. Five seconds. He grabbed her hand and said: "My name is Gabriel." As the train entered he got up and ran to the empty waiting room behind the platform, shut the door, threw the bag down, blessed himself, fell on it and embraced the bag as one would embrace a lover.

- **Daniel Tierney**

12

Succession

Dazed, frustrated, her wings barely carrying her heavy abdomen full of eggs and honey, she dropped onto the landing board and sashayed inside. The workers greeted the stranger, and in her lemongrass perfume, they smelled an opportunity. Their queen was slowing down, a problem the workers disagreed about all summer. One faction built a cup, preparing to replace her, and another tore it down. Their indecision could prove fatal if their queen died mid-winter or failed to produce enough workers to survive the cold. The queen who just walked in, however, was young and strong. Rather than fight her off as the intruder she was, the workers showed her to the nest, fanning her fragrance around the colony.

The queen is the mother of all the workers, but not their leader. Instead, workers make decisions about the life of the colony democratically. Highly attuned to temperature, light, population, and pheromones, the workers may decide to swarm, splitting the colony, half leaving with the original queen to find a new home. If they suspect something is wrong with their queen, they raise a new one. The workers control the temperature of the nest, prompting the queen to lay more eggs after the winter solstice, building the colony for spring. They adjust the size of cells in the honeycomb, indicating if the queen should lay eggs for more workers or the larger drones. Worker bees move through a series of jobs, from undertaker to forager, and one of the roles they might fill is as part of the queen's entourage, following her, grooming her, feeding her. Whereas queens of some species, such as bumblebees, overwinter alone, the colony sustains honeybee queens. Without the queen laying eggs, the colony will dwindle and die, but without workers, the queen cannot survive either.

The young queen, Hippolyta, was only two months old. The workers in her colony raised her in a peanut-shaped cell, feeding her royal jelly through her larval stage, then sealing her up to finish her transformation into a virgin queen. She was not the only virgin. The first to emerge, she was relieved to discover that none of her sisters had hatched. She would not have to do battle, just quiet assassination. As the workers around her spread the news, she located the cells of her twelve pupating rivals and tore them open, stinging the bees inside. She was the queen of this colony.

Although the queen's entourage and larger size help the beekeeper find her, placing a dot of paint on her thorax can make her easier to spot. To mark her, I was supposed to capture Hippolyta in a plastic clip and then transfer her to a tube with a grate at one end. With a foam plunger, I would nudge her against the grate and put a yellow dot—indicating that she was born in a year ending in two—on her thorax. Three times, I tried and failed to shut her in the tube. She escaped. Examining the ground closely before each step, I searched, but never found her. I hoped that she flew back inside, disappearing into the mass of workers. On my next hive inspection, I found nine queen cells. Hippolyta was lost and the bees were replacing her.

The boldest and quickest, Hippolyta II, hatched first to tear open her sisters' cells. On the next sunny morning, she flew away to mate but never returned. The workers whispered to each other; as their anxiety grew, they imagined magpies snatching the queen from the air or truck windshields carrying her away, further than she could fly. There were no more eggs, and as the evenings cooled, they wondered how they would make it to winter.

When I discovered that the new queen had not started laying, I knew that the bees were out of time to successfully requeen, even if I gave them eggs from my second hive. The best option was to combine the two colonies, giving them a large population and a single queen to prepare for winter. I searched for the remaining queen but could not find her. Carefully, I stacked the boxes from one hive on top of the other, placing a layer of newspaper between them, allowing the bees to get used to the idea of each other, spreading the queen's pheromones around the hive, covering all the workers with a common identity, before they chewed through the paper and accepted each other as family.

A strange barrier stood in the middle of their hive, but from the other side, a soothing fragrance—a lemony scent that made the bees feel safe and at home. Their queen had returned. She brought strangers, but that did not tarnish the miracle. Her daughters set to work tearing down the wall, eating through its waxy, crinkly texture and dragging out the pieces, leaving the debris like ashes that their queen had risen from. Nothing soothed their anxiety like working toward a common task and as they worked, they welcomed the strangers as sisters.

A week later, I opened the hive to see if the colonies had combined and if the queen was laying eggs. In the nest stood a big, beautiful, suspiciously familiar queen, surrounded by attentive workers. I compared her to photos in my records and confirmed my initial suspicion. Queen Hippolyta I—who I thought I lost—was back in her hive. "But how?" I whispered. Did the bees immediately kill the old queen when a new one landed at their door or did they let her live a little longer? Mother and daughter queens do sometimes briefly coexist. I imagined their buzzing as a story of a young queen walking into the wrong colony and being handed the keys by an old, tired queen, her estranged mother. Of how she came home weeks later, bringing her new subjects with her, to the relief of her daughters, who were certain they would perish without her.

- **Kasey Butcher Santana**

Serpents

Marion believed it was like the way certain people approached God, stricken by the fear of death before surrendering to the promise of an afterlife. It was the same with snakes. When one looked into the face of Marion's sister, Ramona, the creature would flick its tongue and coil and rattle. And then, meeting the looming eyes of Marion, the viper would retreat into the stillness of submission.

The sister's alchemy had never failed them. They would need their harmonious gifts more than ever that morning with the rattlesnake at the Colbert's place. It'd already bitten the family dog, and now the pet was on its way to an emergency clinic in Roseville. The attacker had slithered under a pyramid of pallets between the propane tank and the doughboy pool.

"I want that thing dead," said Reed Colbert.

He was a short and compressed man whose face and voice had the capacity to be gentle if a snake hadn't just bitten his dog and he wasn't drunk. It was a woman, perhaps a wife or daughter, who'd called the sisters and asked them to come out and capture and move the rattler. This person had a different world view of animals than Reed and was apparently the one transporting the dog to the vet.

"That's not what we do," said Ramona. She went to her knees in front of the pile of pallets, craning her neck and peering into the voids as if she were trying to read an ancient inscription. "We relocate. We do not kill. We capture the snake. Then we take it to a location where it has a chance of surviving."

The rattler would be freed on a place called Deason Ranch, 1200 hundred acres of oak woodland next to the Colbert's land and owned by a local land trust. Its caretaker was an eccentric and somewhat scary character named Glenn Hyde, who lived alone in the old ranch house. There were other release sites, but this snake needed to go to Glenn Hyde at Deason Ranch. Snakes were relocated as close to the capture site as possible and within the same habitat type, perhaps even inside the animal's home-range. It would still be tough going for the reptile in its new biological neighborhood, but the sisters believed the rattler would have a better chance of surviving its new terrain rather than facing the blade of a shovel or the spray of a shotgun.

~~~

Reed Colbert gave up on the snake's death sentence. His anger turned to fascination. He shuffled close enough to Ramona and the pallets that she could smell whatever it was he'd been drinking.

"So, Reed," said Marion. "How about you just go into the house and let us do this?"

"All right," he said. "But I want that thing gone."

They waited until Reed was inside and showed his face in the window. The snake's rattle sounded like a steady hard rain on a metal roof. Marion could see its tongue, flashing through the dark spaces in the pallets. Ramona stood nearby and held a homemade hook in her left hand, a piece of three-quarter-inch PVC pipe she'd shaped at the end with the heat of an acetylene torch. In her other hand was the snare, also homemade: another piece of PVC tailored and threaded with a looped rope at one end and a triggered handle at the other. Marion had placed a wooden crate between her and her sister. Marion had built the crate.

"You ready?" Ramona said.

"Ready," said Marion. They moved closer to the pallets and Ramona peeled them away until the snake was in the open. "Oh my," said Marion. "He's a bruiser."

It was the biggest western rattlesnake (*Crotalus oreganus oreganus*) the sisters had seen, and they'd lost count of the number of snakes they'd captured and relocated over the years. During that time they'd learned a lot about the reptiles and came to respect their traits and their vital place in nature. The sisters believed the creature was unfairly maligned and its lethality overstated, notwithstanding whatever fate awaited the Colbert's dog.

After Ramona had excited the rattler, Marion edged closer and stared into its eyes. She was nearer the animal than most people would have considered safe, but though it was the biggest one they'd ever seen, its behavior was no different. She'd come to accept the paranormal nature of her interaction with the vipers, and to acknowledge the power of unseen forces. It was as if the snake had a soul, peculiar, but something with spirit and energy she was able to bridge with her vision. The word "magical" couldn't do it justice, making it seem petty and worldly, a trick performed by an entertainer. And she had reasons to believe there was nothing more to the snake's behavior than the random spin of evolution, molecules arranged by survival, chance. She'd spent 15 years as a neonatal ICU nurse at a university hospital. Her experiences there –witnessing such a strange mix of the supernatural and what seemed like the cold indifference of a godless, material world –had ended her quest for theological answers to things. She remained suspended in a kind of purgatory of faith, resigned to a reality of purposelessness, but then restored into believing in a higher power whenever she and her sister did what they did with the rattlers.

She held her gaze on the snake. Her eyes calmed the creature enough to allow Ramona to thrust the hooked PVC pipe around its body and jerk it from the pallets and capture it in her snare. It'd become something Marion loved to watch, like a splendid dance or a circus act. Marion slid the wooden crate closer. Then Ramona placed the snake inside and Marion shut and latched the lid.

Marion lifted the crate and Ramona followed her to the truck. Ramona had built a special frame in the bed so the crate wouldn't slide around on the rough and winding roads they often traveled. Reed came out of the house. Marion told him they'd captured the snake and she hoped their dog would be all right. Reed had more to drink while inside. He slurred a thank you and waved goodbye as Ramona stepped on the gas and threw up some gravel behind her wheels.

Whenever they performed a capture without either of them getting bit, the sisters felt better about everything. It was as if they'd shared a joyful memory or laughed at a joke no one else got.

They'd lived together for nine years now. Marion had moved up from Woodland where she'd had the nursing job. She threw away a cushy State retirement and a lively life near a vibrant and liberal university town to come and live with her older sister. She'd had relationships with men, but her partners all seemed to have "issues." Ramona told her it was the nurse in her that drew her to these needy males. "They're like your ICU babies," Ramona had said.

Marion couldn't argue with her sister. When it came to judging men, Ramona had done very well. Her husband, Kyle, had been as close to being the perfect man a woman could imagine. He was ruggedly handsome but had a soft, empathetic voice that belied his hard, outdoorsy look. He taught second grade at the same elementary school where Ramona had taught. It was how they met. He played banjo in a local bluegrass band. Every year he grew a bounty of pickling cucumbers and pickled 100 quarts of what he called "Kyle's Dills" and sold them at the local Farmer's Market. The label on the jar was a picture of Kyle playing a banjo with a pickle protruding from his lips like a green cigar. He'd been an avid cyclist and involved in the local cycling community. He often rode with a group on Sundays, but the day he was struck and killed he was riding alone. He was on a narrow highway out of town. A vehicle slammed into him and hurled his broken body into a thicket of manzanita, where he was found by a passing motorist hours later. It was a hit and run. No witnesses. The driver was never identified. Ramona and Marion had offered a reward for information about the incident, but they'd never received anything that amounted to much. Ramona's grief was paralyzing and so deep Marion stayed with her, returning to her job at the ICU until a perfect storm of Ramona's deep mourning and Marion's own moroseness about her job led the sisters to share Ramona's home until it became naturally permanent instead of a deliberative choice. And now it felt more right than ever, especially after they discovered their concordant talents with the snakes.

~~~

They hit the gravel road to Deason Ranch. Not long after they saw the old ranch house ahead of them, they heard Jimi Hendrix's version of *All Along the Watchtower*. Then they saw Glenn Hyde on the front porch, shirtless and in flowery shorts and playing air-guitar. He had long, Santa Claus white hair. It twirled like a sheet in a clothes drier. He was tall and thin. Once Marion said she didn't know how his pants stayed on.

They pulled up in front of the house and waited for the song to end and for Glenn's body to stop spinning. Glenn was the older brother of the land trust's executive director. The sisters, along with just about everyone else, surmised Glenn was given the "job" of caretaker because of the family connection. His duties were limited. The ranch did have cows on it–free range, grass-fed Angus –but it was under a lease arrangement, and the rancher took care of absolutely everything having to do with the cattle. Apparently Glenn didn't even know how to ride a horse.

Glenn saw the sisters but still held the invisible guitar in his hands. He became the perfect image of an eccentric recluse banished to a remote piece of land for the land's sake, and his own.

The sisters had released only one other snake on the ranch, about two years ago. Glenn had seemed indifferent about it. But he'd followed them on his ATV to the release site, his long white hair dancing in the wind. He looked like a hero in a biblical myth coming to life in Ramona's rear-view mirror, an image evoked by the sisters' religious upbringing. Their father had been the pastor of a Four-Square church, the one founded by the charismatic evangelist, Aimee McPherson. He presided there for 12 years until his doubts about the church grew into an untenable relationship with its hierarchy and he began his own non-denominational fellowship in the basement of a hardware store. He was a gifted speaker, but didn't employ the theatrics of a revivalist preacher and rarely spoke of hell, sin, or damnation. Then, when the sisters were in high school, their mother was sitting at the dinner table and collapsed like a felled tree and died instantly on the kitchen floor from a brain aneurism. Not long after, they witnessed their father's transition into a murkier form of Christianity. They were old enough and smart enough to see how his grief stabbed at his theology. Sometimes they'd find their father asleep in the recliner in the living room of their little house, with books by men with weird sounding names, like Soren Kierkegaard and Baruch Spinoza, spread open on his lap. Soon the change in his views about God made its way into his sermons and he couldn't hold onto his conservative flock and he gave up the ministry altogether. Still, after all this, the sisters believed their father never lost his faith, but only that it was made more whole and thoughtful and real by a deeper investigation of its nature, and the source of his doubts. He left the sisters with the enduring message to have the courage to change and seek the truth, even if it made life difficult.

~~~

Glenn dropped his invisible guitar and left the porch and approached the truck.

"Hello, Glenn," said Ramona.

"Do I know you?" he said.

It could have been a hostile question, but Glenn's soft tone and the passive tilt of his head made it sincere and innocent. Before Ramona could answer, Glenn craned his neck to look at the crate in the back of the pickup. "Oh yeah, you're the snake ladies," he said.

"Yes, we are," said Ramona.

He took his eyes off the crate and peered into the cab at Marion. She felt his gaze and pretended to be studying a map. Then Glenn straightened himself and put his hands on his waist and stepped away from the truck, as if he were about to give a speech.

"Did you know I used to be a marriage counselor?" he said.

"Is that right?" said Ramona.

There were stories about Glenn, but his being a marriage counselor wasn't one of them. The stories, or gossip, only made Glenn's imbalances even harder to classify. One common tale was that he'd once delved into experimental drugs, pursuing Timothy O'Leary's hallucinogenic adventures, but with a kind of recklessness that left him permanently impaired. The more crass gossipers simply claimed Glenn was "bat shit crazy," a phrase both Ramona and Marion had heard more than once from different people. Glenn's brother, no doubt the most intimate with Glenn's mysterious life, had assured the sisters his brother was only "a little eccentric" and they'd have nothing to fear from him when they released a rattler on the land trust property. "Your snakes are far more dangerous than my brother," he'd said.

"Well, it's true," Glenn continued. "Problem was I couldn't practice what I preached. I've been divorced three times."

Glenn held up three fingers. There wasn't a trace of regret in his voice. Instead, it was as if he'd just announced he'd once been a contestant on Jeopardy. The sisters didn't know or care whether Glenn was telling the truth. When he began to explain why he thought the marriages hadn't worked out, Ramona sensed his ramblings would turn epic and so she tactfully cut him off and Glenn didn't seem to mind. He looked at the crate again. "So where are you going to put this one?" he said.

They didn't have a site picked out. Their plan was to survey the ranch for a spot that matched the snake's habitat at the Colbert's.

"We thought we'd just look around for a place," said Ramona. "Is that all right?"

"Yes," he said. "But I'm going with you."

Glenn climbed into the back of the pickup.

"What is he *doing?*" mumbled Marion.

Ramona craned her neck out the window.

"Might get a little rough back there, Glenn," she said.

"I know," Glenn said. "I live here, remember? Proceed."

There were several jeep trails and narrow roads on the ranch. All necessitated a four-wheel drive with high clearance. So it would indeed be a bumpy ride for Glenn, who, at first, insisted on standing in the bed with his legs apart, as if he were trying to prove he could defy the laws of gravity. It wasn't until Ramona hit one of the deeper pot holes and Glenn nearly flopped over the tailgate when Glenn was forced to sit.

They came to an old corral and cattle chute. This marked the place where the sister's would decide which way to go with the rattler. The last time they were here, they'd traveled to the west, bouncing down a hillside to a dry creek bed cutting through a scattering of scrub oak, where they'd released the snake. But there was plenty of habitat on the ranch matching the Colbert's, and Ramona didn't have to drive far before finding a good release site. They parked on a shaded knoll. Dry seasonal drainages joined at the base of the hill. It was ideal landscape for the rattler: open rocky areas for basking, plenty of rodent burrows, expanses of tall grass for protected movement and patches of brush for shade and cover. But they'd need to hike down the rocky slope to the site, and Glenn insisted on carry the crate with the snake in it.

The sisters walked on each side of him, not at all confident in his teetering, spindly legs. "Right there," said Ramona, pointing to a small moraine of silt on the edge of the drainage. "Let's go there."

This prompted Glenn to pick up his pace. Marion told him to slow down, but he didn't.

He set the crate down on the spot. "So now what?" he said.

"Well," said Ramona. "Now we let it go."

She dragged the crate closer to a number of hollowed out shrub roots the rattler might slither into once freed. She'd brought along her homemade hook and used it to open the crate's latch.

It'd turned hot. Streams of sweat ran down Glenn's chest, forming a fan of glittering tributaries all the way to his waist. Again Ramona used her tool, this time to tip the opened crate over and then lift it off the snake. The viper remained in a tight coil but its rattle was steady and loud.

Glenn squatted to look at it.

"Not too close, Glenn," Ramona said.

"Why doesn't it leave?" he said.

"It will," said Marion. "But we're done here."

Marion picked up the crate and the sisters began their walk back to the truck, thinking Glenn was right behind them, but he wasn't. They turned around to find him yet closer to the animal. He looked as if he were sleeping standing up, his arms hanging limp at his side and his head bowed. Seeing Glenn like this plunged Marion into a memory of a father in the ICU standing and praying over a newborn son who'd entered the world with a congenital heart defect. The child had been rushed to surgery in its first hours of life and was expected to live, but not long after Marion had seen the father praying day in and day out, the child died unexpectedly. It was this –the way hope had been so elevated, only to be ravaged – that sent her beliefs reeling. In the days after, she tried to be inspired by her own father's spiritual resilience after her mother's death, and how he had not lost his faith. Sometimes she acquired his strength. Sometimes she didn't. And now, seeing the way Glenn stood next to the snake, like that dad praying over his sick son, it was all there again, pulling in her doubts like some emotional black hole, leaving her unable to speak when Glenn reached out to grab the rattler.

Ramona did holler at Glenn, but only after he'd grabbed the snake just below its head. He held it out with a straight arm and at eye level and he stared at it as if he were sending it a telepathic message. He stomped off into the brush with the viper twisting and twirling beneath his grip.

The sisters stood still, both waiting for the other to do something. Then Glenn emerged from the shrubbery and swiped his hands against his flowery shorts to remove the snake's slime. Without pausing or saying a word he marched past the sisters up the hill and climbed back into the bed of the pickup. He sat on the closed tailgate and waved at them, his white hair hanging like a wet mop over his shoulders. He stared off into the distance, as if nothing at all extraordinary had happened.

The sisters, especially Marion, were too stunned by what they'd just witnessed to speak of it until after they'd dropped Glenn off at the ranch house and were on their way home.

They took the long way back, thinking that adding unnecessary miles to the drive would help them sort out whatever it was they'd just seen.

"Was that, like, a dream or something?" said Ramona.

"No."

"Maybe we should have made sure he didn't get bit."

"He didn't."

"Well, next time he's not going with us."

"No way."

This was the extent of it: nothing more than a very strange occurrence by a very strange man who'd escaped injury purely out of luck. They went from wondering about how and why Glenn had managed to grab the snake without getting bit, to whether he was lying about being a marriage counselor, and his three divorces.

After a time they realized what road they were on and how far out of their way they'd traveled. It seemed they'd been lifted out of space and time and all of a sudden found themselves on a highway neither of them really wanted to be on, especially Ramona. It was the road where Ramona's husband Kyle had been killed. For a few years there had been a white cross marking the spot. Ramona had put it there, but after a time it mysteriously disappeared and she wouldn't replace it. But she knew the location like she knew the color of her eyes. She slowed as they went past. For the first time in years she looked deep into the terrain, as if it were the face of a bully threatening someone she loved. Marion watched her sister and said *look out, Ramona*, when their truck veered slightly over the road's centerline. Ramona corrected her course and told Marion she was sorry. Marion said there was nothing to be sorry about.

At home Marion made dinner while Ramona sat under the shade of an oak in the backyard. Marion watched her sister from the kitchen window and could tell the drive past the place Kyle had been killed had affected her. Ramona sat still and stared off. It'd always been hard for Marion to see her big sister hurting and trying to pretend she wasn't. As girls, Ramona always wanted to portray herself as the strong one. When their mother died, and then their father, Ramona took care of business and never revealed her pain, no crying, always stoic and logical. But it was different with Kyle. It was the first time Marion had seen her sister weep and in need of something or someone beyond herself.

Marion brought the food out and they ate under the tree. That spring, Acorn Woodpeckers had colonized the sprawling branches. The birds squawked in the limbs but the sisters ignored them. Ramona didn't speak until they'd finished eating dinner and the night cooled and the light dimmed. Then she talked about Kyle, how much she missed him, and the many wonderful things they'd done together. Marion let Ramona carry on and said nothing, moved to silence by the lift of her sister's spirits.

After dark they went back to the house. Ramona climbed into bed but Marion returned to the backyard and sat beneath the oak. A soothing breeze rattled the dense quiet. Before long she drifted into a shallow slumber and had a fleeting dream of the eccentric caretaker holding the snake and marching boldly across an open field.

- John Thomson

Simultaneous

It is like when the pieces
of ice fell lightly
from the sky
on my head,
the daffodil in a
plastic flowerpot
in my hand,
and the gray
engine of my truck
covered in yellow
pollen at the grocery
store when I
thought that
winter had passed.

I had seen the fox
and her two babies
near the horses,
the pine trees,
the big white house,
and the cemetery,
about a week before
I saw three white
crosses from a
car accident
on the side of
a different road.

I remember seeing
a fireman die in
a health clinic
from bee stings
in a poor country
at about the same
time that my
wife was pregnant.
An orange sun
goes down
and a full moon rises.

-Benjamin Nash

Cutting In

Soha has a wrist full of scars lined up like railroad ties—
welts of freedom.

She hides in her black hoodie, head buried in hands,
shoulders heaving sobs. Grabs for the box of tissue,
a bottle of water, my listening ear—
inept offerings.

She tells me a story in this quiet, dim light,
a story no other teacher hears:

The Taliban that did half the job—
that car bomb, a scorch of shrapnel fire searing
a littered street in Kabul like a righteous knife.
Soha's grandfather in scattered knots never gathered.
Her father, the driver, in a coma, caught in a sluice
of dulled terror ten years later. He still hides.

Soha wants to bring her father home. Wants to protect her family.
Everyone but herself. Her razor cutting in. Fresh blood-red flowing—
a torch like running feet   away.

- Carrie Kornacki

24

Three Loaves

Mairéad woke early in the morning and began milling, mixing, kneading, scoring, and baking. The children of her creation were born at dawn and sold by dusk. Kupel's was a Jewish bakery, though Mairéad had never been to synagogue herself. Her husband Alphonse was born to German-Jewish Treblinka survivors, an association that suitably authenticated her claim of "authentic" Challah bread to her patrons. His only request was that the store be closed from Friday to Saturday, sundown to sundown, and she was only too happy to oblige him. Kupel's was the premier destination for Jewish baked goods in all of Dublin, though that was admittedly not saying much.

The dough was stubborn today. She sat nursing her knuckles and sipping tea, watching the canal through the front window of the store as it burned golden in the rising sunlight and settled back into its murky green. The room was filled with malty warmth, sweet calm. The bursts of key-clacks began from Alphonse's typewriter in the back room and Mairéad knew it was time. She unlocked the front door and flipped the vinyl sign to read, "Open."

It wasn't long before Eileen came for her usual Wednesday morning pickup. She burst into the store halfway through her first sentence.

"--are you now, Mairéad?"

"Ah you know yourself. I've got your sourdough here for you. Freshly baked." She rolled shut the waxed paper bag.

"Cheers, thanks for that." Eileen placed a tenner on the counter. "Colm's after getting a new car."

"Is that right? That's exciting."

"He winds himself up for nothing. He loves his car. More likely it is that he grows wheels than that he replaces it. And the boys would have an absolute fit, they love that thing."

"And how are they?"

"They're at the age now where they don't want me to baby them but they don't mind my doing their laundry and cooking their meals, you know how it is," Eileen said, waving her hand. "Oh my goodness, I didn't mean--"

"You're all right," Mairéad said. "Alphonse and I made a choice is all."

"Right so."

The money sat between them, Eileen's fingernails tapping across it.

"Was there... something else?"

"I hate to mention it, you know me, it's not my place and all that," she said. "But there's a little girl out front who asked me if I had a Euro."

"Oh?"

"It was all very unpleasant." Eileen tilted in. "Asking for money, imagine. And you know how these ones can get. I figured it's your store, better for you to sort it out. Not my business, like."

Mairéad made change and thanked her. She waited for Eileen to walk out of sight down the street before peeking through the glass door. The girl was no older than eleven, maybe twelve. She wore neon-pink fleece trousers and a matching zip-up, both streaked and unwashed. She was hunched over an ant on the concrete, pivoting as it moved to watch it walk.

Mairéad stepped outside. The girl stood. There was a scab of mucous under her nose. Her face was dirty. They waited, each daring the other to speak.

"This is my bakery," Mairéad finally said.

"Good for you."

"This is my bakery," she repeated, firmer.

"You want a medal?"

Mairéad considered the girl. "Do you maybe want something to eat?"

"Something to eat? And what would I be doing out here if I had money to eat," she said, and kicked the pavement. "I haven't got any money, have I?"

"There's no need to be nasty."

"I am'nt. What a stupid question. Do I want something to eat?"

"If I give you something to eat, will you go away?"

She considered the question.

"I'm Mairéad." The girl stared. "And what's your name?"

"Gráinne," she said. "Like the pirate queen."

Mairéad held the door open and the girl came into the bakery. She inspected the walls, staying at each photograph a moment before moving onto the next. Her mouth was a tight line, unimpressed.

"We've got cakes and pastries. Whatever you like."

She leaned into a sepia photograph of Alphonse's family, him as a little boy, their heads capped with yarmulkes. "This some kinda Jew shop or something?"

"That's enough of that."

"I'm just asking." Gráinne made her way to the front display case, looking across the breads and pastries with wide eyes. She pointed at a gleaming loaf of braided bread towards the back of the top shelf. "Whassthat?"

"It's called Challah."

"Looks like my Ma's bread." She kept her nose pressed against the glass, staring at the loaf.

"I'll cut you some." Mairéad sawed a thick slice from the loaf. She wrapped it in a paper napkin. Gráinne reached for it, and Mairéad pulled back.

"If you're hungry you can come in here but I don't want you hanging about. And if you tell anyone, if anyone else comes looking for a handout, if you bring anyone with you, the deal's off straight away and I'll be calling the Gards. Am I understood?"

"All right," Gráinne said.

"Am I understood?"

"All right, I said." Gráinne chewed and swallowed and only then seemed to taste it. Her face wrinkled up.

"What's wrong?"

"That's rotten that is," she said. "That doesn't taste like my Ma's bread at all."

Mairead tore a piece from the loaf and stuck it in her mouth, chewing carefully. "I baked it fresh this morning--"

"I wouldn't even feed that to the birds. A bleedin' pigeon wouldn't even eat that."

"Now hang on a minute, there's no--"

"That's turned my stomach. I'm not even hungry anymore." She threw the rest of the slice into the bin. "That's not like my Ma's bread at all."

Mairéad opened her mouth but Gráinne was faster than her words. The small bell above the hinge rang as it drifted shut, the only sound in the sudden silence left in the girl's wake. Mairéad stared at the closed door, fuming. She wanted to grab that brat by fistfuls of her charity-shop fleece and scream in her face. She wanted to slap that little bitch upside the head. Mairéad sat down on her stool with a groan. More than that, she wanted to know where the girl would go now and if she had something to eat for dinner.

~ ~ ~

Alphonse yawned and shuffled the stack of onionskin pages in his hands, evening them out against the duvet.

"I think I'm getting somewhere with this story."

Mairéad nodded. She put a finger on the page of her cookbook and scribbled something into her notepad.

"Are we having kugel for Shabbat dinner?" he asked.

"Chicken soup."

"We had chicken soup last week. We always have chicken soup."

"So what do you want?"

He perked up. "Really?"

Mairéad traced her finger further down the page. "Why not. You pick."

"Even... brisket?" he asked.

"I can make a brisket."

"Brisket and kugel?"

"Now you're being cheeky," she said. "Keep that up and you'll be getting chicken soup."

"Fine, fine." He nodded towards the cookbook. "Are you trying something new?"

"No," she said. "The Challah isn't coming out how I want it to."

"I love your Challah. Everyone loves your Challah."

"A little girl came in, couldn't have been but ten. She said it was the worst thing she'd ever tasted."

"Who ever got any use out of listening to the opinions of a child?"

"It's not good enough," she said.

"So tell me." Alphonse placed his glasses on the bedside table. "Tell me what this infant tasted in your world class bread that your husband, who's tasted Challah from Wrocław to Galway, wouldn't know."

"Why, so I can bore you to sleep?"

"No, no, of course not," he said, groaning as he lay down. "Tell me because it's got you riled up and you're my wife and so it's got me riled up." He yawned. "Don't you see how riled up I am?"

"I usually make it in the morning, but your one here in this cookbook seems to think you're better off leaving it in the fridge overnight. 'The character of the bread takes on a richer sense of depth given the extra time to coalesce.' So she says."

"Wouldn't want a shallow sense of depth. Not in your bread."

"I went to that expensive shop in town and picked up honey from Cork. It's pricey, but worth it I think. That and the free range eggs for the wash before it goes into the oven. Your one says to let it come to room temperature before brushing it on for extra gloss."

"Extra gloss." Alphonse yawned, his eyelids fluttering shut. "Of course, you can't forget the extra gloss."

"Alphonse?"

"Mairéad," he said.

She thought of the girl's face, her round cheeks. About what she must have been like as a baby. The words stuck in her mouth like dry cake.

Alphonse's father had been a brutal man. They all were back then, he made sure to say whenever the topic came up. Alphonse believed that violence was a learned trait that was passed from father to son. His father was not a violent man until Alphonse was born and something was unlocked inside of him, some hidden rage that had been dormant all his life. And it was true that in moments of pure frustration a shade of something unfamiliar would pass over his face. But it passed, she told him over and over. It always passed. Early in their marriage, Mairéad would test the topic every few months and Alphonse would push it away. The years that followed finalized their tentative decision.

"Go on." Alphonse smacked his lips. "What is it?"

She watched him drift asleep. He looked so peaceful in the lamplight. Her husband. Her family. "It can wait another night," she said and kissed his forehead.

~~~

How slowly time could pass. People hadn't even started walking their dogs yet. The dog-walkers came first, then the carriage-toting mothers, and then Alphonse's typewriter. Always in that order.

Mairéad had done everything right. What now sat on the top shelf of her display case was the most magnificent shining loaf of bread that she had ever baked. Did it look best on the top row or should she center it? That little ingrate's eyes would surely pop out of her head. She might cry it would be so tasty, the crumb so delicate. This would be a decisive victory. Hers was the best Challah in Dublin. Even a child wouldn't be able to argue with that, even this child.

A woman pushed a carriage along the canal. Alphonse's keys clacked from the back room. The bell above the door rang and Mairéad sat a little straighter, but it was only Eileen.

"--never believe what happened to me, you'll never guess. I'm driving home yesterday and I park out front of the house, you know. And I step out of the car with that loaf of sourdough bread you gave me."

Something pink blurred past the glass door.

"That bread smells so gorgeous that I can't wait, I peel back the paper and rip off a bit. Just a corner, like."

Mairéad peered over Eileen's shoulder as she spoke.

"Once it's in the house it goes like that. Between Colm and the kids I'm lucky to even get a slice. So I rip off a corner of it and then I hear this screech and I look up and this great big seagull is bearing down on me. Oh my goodness, I didn't know what to do."

The pink shape passed across the front window and disappeared below it.

"The bread slipped out of the paper and right onto the road. Can you believe that? Mairéad, I said can you believe that?"

"Oh, that's nice," she said.

"It isn't nice at all, actually."

"Sorry. That's not nice." She shook her head. "You'll need another sourdough, then?"

"Well, yes." Eileen tutted her tongue against her teeth. "I'm lucky I didn't get hurt you know. Some poor woman out in Galway lost her eye to a seagull once. It was in the papers."

"Absolutely." Mairéad wrapped the sourdough in wax paper, staring out the window as she made change.

"Could have pecked my eyes out," Eileen said. "Both my eyes out, even." She shook her head as she left.

Mairéad waited behind the counter until Eileen disappeared from view, then stood. No, maybe it was better to wait. She sat back down and tapped her foot. She took a sip of her tea. It was well cold. The decision was impossible. Stand or sit. Confront or wait. The door creaked open and the bell above the hinge rang.

"Hullo?" Gráinne called in.

"Well Jaysis, come in if you're coming in," Mairéad said. Her heart thumped.

Gráinne wore the same outfit as the day before. She was too young for the dark circles traced beneath her eyes. Mairéad waved the girl over to the counter.

"A promise is a promise," she said. "Go on, pick something out. I made a fresh Challah."

Gráinne pressed her nose against the glass. "This one taste like dog shite too?"

"It's free food, isn't it? I've welcomed you into my bakery, haven't I?"

"All right," she said.

"You're lucky to get this for free. You're lucky to get it at all. I'm known for it, actually. People come from all over town for my Challah. I pride myself on it."

"Wouldn't be too proud of that myself." She stared at the baked goods, then pointed out a flapjack.

"Oh," Mairéad said. "Are you sure?"

"You said I could pick."

"I did, you can, I just--"

"I want that one there. Unless it's got raisins. I hate raisins. I'd rather eat a flip flop. Might as well eat a rat turd than a raisin."

"No," Mairéad said. "There aren't raisins." She fished the flapjack out from the case and wrapped it in wax paper, handing it over the counter.

Gráinne turned to go.

"Wait," Mairéad said. She pulled the glossy loaf of Challah from the case and carved a slice, wrapping it in a napkin.

"I don't want that," Gráinne said. "I want the flapjack."

"Just eat it. I'm the one handing out free food, aren't I?"

Gráinne eyed the bread. "What'd you put in it?"

"Oh, just try it."

"All right, fine," she said, taking the slice. The bread crumbled around her lips as she bit into it. She chewed and swallowed.

"Well?"

The girl shook her head. "That's actually worse," she said, tossing it into the bin. "I don't know how it could be worse, but it is. No wonder nobody comes in here."

"Stop that now," Mairéad said. "I've done everything I could to--"

"My Ma's bread was better. I've got the flapjack at least to get the taste of shite outta my mouth," she laughed, pulling open the door and slipping back out.

~ ~ ~

Mairéad couldn't focus. She spent five minutes re-reading the same page before setting it down, defeated. She tapped her foot against the tiles. She came out from behind the counter and wandered around her shop. What did her customers see when they came into her store? What did they think of her? She wandered from the store into the apartment. Alphonse's office door was open just wide enough to see the desk and the typewriter. He had left for his daily walk already and wouldn't be back for at least another hour. She set her hand against the wood and pushed.

30

The door creaked open.

Alphonse didn't like when Mairéad came in his office. He'd never said it out loud--he didn't say many things out loud--but it was something nonetheless that Mairéad knew. Alphonse was a quiet person and quiet people, Mairéad had learned, spoke as much in their silences as in their words. She tiptoed to his desk. A piece of paper was wound halfway through the typewriter. A neat stack stood next to it. She'd bought him a laptop once and he even let her take him through the word processing program on it. She found it in its box a week later, untouched. "I like what I like," he said and shrugged. Though Alphonse would read her things he'd written if she asked, he didn't like to share his writing. He wrote for himself, he'd told her, and not for anyone else.

Mairéad lifted the papers from the desk. Alphonse was a gentle writer. He assembled his sentences like a child plucking leaves in a garden. His phrasing held an awkward quality that had a certain type of unintended beauty. He wrote about baseball players and bullfighters, astronauts and presidents. Once and only once had he shared some writing about his parents and the town he grew up in.

But this story was different. It was about a teenager coming home from his first semester of university. His mother was unable to reconcile this newer more adult version of her child and mourned their lost relationship. The father experienced the opposite. He was able for the first time to understand his son. And when he returned to school the parents were changed, their dynamic inverted. It was a tender story full of love. Mairéad set the pages back down just as she found them and returned to the front of the store. She sat on her stool waiting for the day to pass and found that her hand was trembling.

~~~

The next morning, Mairéad scoured the backs of her cabinets for forgotten ingredients. The flour that was months old. The forgotten eggs that were bought at the newsagent, stacked above the jelly worms. The yeast packets that were out of date. She flipped every beautiful step of her recipe. Olive oil gave bread a pillowy lightness so she went with canola instead for the greasy texture. A brioche required a light touch so she hammered the hell out of it. Her complicated recipe was stripped to its barest parts. What did this girl know about baking, anyway? No, she had clearly never tasted something awful enough to warrant spitting out. The dough was sticky and unmanageable and Mairéad wrestled it into submission. She settled on three braids instead of four, stopping herself from so much as brushing it down with an egg wash before it went into the oven. The resulting loaf was dull, flat, and spiteful.

Gráinne poked her head into the store later that morning.

"Haven't you got any other clothes?" Mairéad said.

The girl ignored the question, taking her place in front of the display case. "That flapjack wasn't bad actually, I think I'll have another."

"Why don't you try this first," Mairéad said, and handed over a piece of the Challah.

"That's rotten."

"It's a new recipe."

"New recipe my hole," Gráinne said, and flipped it over in her hand. "Brilliant, it even looks like dog shite."

"Maybe you'd prefer I call the Gards and tell them there's a little girl out of school."

"It's summer ya thick, we're all out of school."

"If you're too scared to try a bit of bread, that's fine, I won't judge."

Gráinne stuck out her tongue.

"Imagine being too scared to try a bit of bread. And here I thought you were supposed to be tough."

"I am not scared! I just don't eat bread that tastes of shite."

A cough came from the door behind the counter. Alphonse stood with his arms crossed. He walked towards the girl and she stepped back. Mairéad looked from Alphonse to Gráinne and thought for a moment that he might actually strike her.

Alphonse kneeled to her level and smiled. "It's okay," he said with a soft voice. "I'll try it with you." He reached forward and broke a corner from her slice. "I'd really appreciate it if you tried it. I'd bet Mairéad over there would even give you another flapjack if you did.   What do you say? I'll even try it with you."

Gráinne thought a second. "Two flapjacks," she said.

Alphonse smiled and nodded. He looked back at Mairéad. "All right then, two flapjacks."

They ate the bread together. Alphonse grimaced as he swallowed and looked back at Mairéad, shaking his head. "I really think you ought to throw out that book," he said.

Gráinne took another bite, and another, until it was gone. Crumbs stuck to her lips. For a moment, Gráinne stood unmoving, a silent revelation unfolding within her. And then the moment passed and the girl dug her hands into her pockets and emptied their contents onto the counter.

"What are you doing?" Mairéad asked.

Gráinne sorted the coins from the candy wrappers and paper receipts and slid them into a pile.

"How much for the rest of it?"

Mairéad considered the misshapen thing on the cutting board that she had been so proud of and now only felt ashamed of having intentionally made something so ugly.

"Wouldn't you rather something nice?"

"Please," Gráinne said. Her eyes were wide and wet.

"Well, how much have you got there?"

The girl hunched over the countertop and counted under her breath as she slid the coins from right to left and then, dissatisfied with the result, started over again. She counted the coins three times and her shoulders fell forward.

"I've only got seventy-eight cents."

"Then it's seventy-eight cents," Mairéad said. She wrapped the loaf in wax paper.

"Thank you," Gráinne said. She took the package and went to leave, then stopped at the door and turned back. "Will you make it again?"

Mairéad nodded.

"Good," Gráinne said.

"Is it like your Ma's?" Mairéad asked.

But Gráinne had already flung the door open and left. Alphonse's keys began to clack from the back room. Mairéad sat trembling on her stool and broke, weeping into her fists as quietly as she could so that her husband wouldn't hear her. Soon she'd have to start cooking.

- James Roseman

War and Fruit Loops

Before. The forbidden word of any trauma. The trick is to look forward, not back. Once you look back, you're fucked. I can hear the ceiling fan whirling above me. But I'm not thinking of choppers or jumping out of them to shoot at foreign faces. I'm not thinking of that. Fuck that. I'm thinking forward to what I'm going to have for breakfast. Stay in the moment my shrink says. So, I'm staying in the moment. I want Froot Loops. Months without Froot Loops. I want to eat Froot Loops for breakfast, lunch, and dinner.

I got the largest box I could find. The bold letters Family Size jump off the box. I don't have a family. Not that I need one. In fact, the last thing I need is a family. It's quiet with just me. No wife, no kids, no parents, just me. Families are loud as fuck, at least that's what I'm told. The guys in the Corp were always bitching about their wives or their kids, and were happy to trade the sound of a screaming baby in the night for the sound of gunfire. Nope. No family needed. Just the box size. I am a fraudulent Froot Loop buyer, I think to myself. A false consumer of Family Size boxes. Heh.

Mick and Nancy will stop by today though. I know this because it's Thursday and Thursday is Nancy's day off. I call it her charity day. She drops by like clockwork to check on me. Like I'm a turkey in the oven. Checking that I'm done, that I'm okay. Okay. Who's okay? If you look at a person. Hard. Any person, and you imagine your fingernails running down their face, peeling the flesh, you can tell. You can see it. They are just as fucked up as the rest of us. They just aren't military-ordered to see a psychiatrist once a week. To sit in an oversized and uncomfortable grey chair with itchy fabric. Don't wear shorts, I tell myself. So I wear long sleeve shirts and my fatigues in the heat of Texas summer to avoid the itch of that fucking chair.

The shrink is nice though. She's not bad. Sometimes I don't hear a word she says. I just watch her lips move. There's something comforting in the movement of her mouth. When she catches me not listening she reminds me of the importance of being in the moment. Be in the moment she says. I guess the past can't bite you in the ass if you're settled in the present. At least that's the idea.

She's nice though. She's not bad. She wears a lot of grey. She fades into her office, which is also grey. Sometimes I imagine she is part of the pale grey wall behind her. A talking wall. I laugh. She wants to know what's funny. I always answer, nothing. I know better than to tell people they look like a wall. I'm careful what I say. You have to be careful what you say. Mick wasn't careful so they took him away. Then he came back. And he came back full of answers to questions I don't give a fuck about. But he wants to share. He wants to save.

"That's a pretty big bowl of Froot Loops! We need to get some greens into your diet. I hope that's not your lunch," Nancy says.

I grind my teeth and say nothing for a moment. I'm tempted to ask why she doesn't get more greens into herself. She's pushing 300 pounds and most of it's self-help jargon

"Your body is your temple." She is wiping invisible crumbs from the counter. Cleaning my already relatively clean kitchen.

Then yours must be a fucking ruin, I think.

"Can I grab a beer, mate?"

Mick's counselor at his rehab was Australian. So now it's 'mate' this, and 'good on ya' that.

I grab him a cold one and crack the top against the counter to open it. I can see Nancy's lips draw into a thin white line of disapproval. I start to whistle. She hates when I whistle. Maybe they'll leave sooner if I keep whistling.

Handing Mick the beer I notice again how gaunt he looks since he 'got healthy'. His skin is wan. He's wearing short gym shorts and a tank top. He looks like a Chia pet, sprouting bright red curls of hair.

This is what you can hope for, I think. Once they trained you to be a soldier, now they train you to be a gaunt chia pet. I'll play their game, win my peace, but I ain't nobody's pet. Not now, not ever.

- A.J. Terlesky

An Old Man and His Dog

Together, one shuffling, the other traipsing,
They amble down the street, the leash slack between them.
Hard to tell who's leading who, perhaps neither,
Just two old friends whiling an afternoon away.
Life has heaped years and burdens on one's shoulders
While robbing the other of his sprightly trot,
But neither seems to care or even notice
Long gone are their days of throw-and-fetch fun.
Out of breath, they stop at a wooden bench,
One resting, the other watching over him;
Wary spectators, they eye the world rush by,
In no haste to return to their empty house.
One more walk together, another blissful day,
Inseparable mates—till it's time for one to go.

- C L Hoang

A Sonoran Desert City

I walk before sunrise through squared-off landscapes
of suburbia, for a while it seems possible
not to think of the dry snarl of heat, the savagery
of manicured lawns, the men and women with bibles
and laws.

Sun bursts through to streets of retreating
liberties hanging by tattered threads, tents
of the unhoused, bus stops as hollow shelter.
We have failed in fatal ways, the vortex
of "civilization" surrounded by sham
choices.

And the desert echoes, exhausted and
endangered. Perhaps the project of humanity
has outlived itself, is winding down.
Perhaps we should give the world back
to the birds and fireflies, the gray wolves
and pygmy owls, the jaguars. Perhaps
we were never the best idea.

- Roxanne Doty

Gray Wolves

I am sorry we didn't pay attention
to the politician who cradles papers
and rationalizations for the end
of your protection.

I am sorry we didn't listen when the philosopher
said to look into your eyes is to see our souls
we stood so close to fake gods we never imagined
your blood could taste the same as our own.

Please keep roaming, crossing sandy soils
of the Chihuahuan and Sonoran surviving
with the wild horses that can't be broken,
the damaged sons and daughters in strength
and stillness fragile like the flame of a candle
before the violent breath of policy.

- **Roxanne Doty**

Fly Girl

My great-grandma Al looks like the spitting image of the sweet old lady from the Sylvester and Tweety bird cartoon, and she too, is far from the guileless granny with the circle-rimmed glasses. She is notorious for catching farts in her hands and giving them as gifts to any child she can lure closely enough to her little, wrinkled hands of mischief.

I am spending my first summer in Porum, Oklahoma as a child.

Porum is a town of 987 people. The population could change at any hour due to the number of its seniors. Gram lives in the super rundown part. It's almost to the point of abandonment and reminds me very much of a Stephen King movie in the making. I can almost taste the laughter of murdered children and corn on my tongue. One bar. One bank. One grocery. The most popular being, the Piggly Wiggly.

I spend a lot of days at the Pig. There is literally nowhere else in town to go, especially in the summertime when the heat magnifies my anxiety. Most 10-year olds don't suffer from debilitating anxiety and depression. I do. I have never known otherwise. When left with too many thoughts to make sense of, I feel like my chest is going to explode. It happens on a dime. Just like when my parents fight. One minute we are watching *Mash,* the next I am dodging glass ashtrays and Asian porn. It escalates so quickly. It makes me so hot inside. I want to scatter and disappear like the pieces of my Operation game.

The manager at the Pig is an older lady, named Doty. She is missing the majority of her teeth, hence her constant whistling. Her favorite song seems to be "Crazy," by Miss Patsy Cline. It makes me crazy. Every day I walk to the Pig through the same two streets: Muskogee and 2nd. I cross the abandoned back alley where Putt-Putt Perry sits next to his old, green bicycle drinking out of a paper bag, bleary-eyed and melancholy. He is as much of a fixture here in Porum as the bank and the Pig. Gram tells me he was hit in the head by a horse when he was younger and "ain't been right since."

I go to the Pig daily to shoplift my favorite candy: grape-flavored Fun Dip. The advertisements in the 80s promised to capture the memories of childhood with its tangy-sweet candy dip powder in nifty 3-flavor combo packs that included 2 candy dipping sticks. The instructions were simple: Dip, Lick, Repeat! I like the candy more than Pop Rocks because I have to work for it a little.

Gram tells me that the manager at The Pig has been bringing her "retarded girl," Nellie to work with her from the day she was born. Together, they sit in the office in front of the store behind two small splintery saloon doors elevated about a foot above the dirty concrete floor. They are surrounded by plexiglass and it looks very much like a sad DJ booth that longs to play Linda Ronstadt songs.

I hate seeing Nellie. Nellie is whom the locals simply refer to as, "the fly girl." It feels like punishment to see her. It feels like karma for all the nights I lay awake and ask God to take me in my sleep. I am an able-bodied kid, yet I'm consumed with thinking of creative ways to accidentally die or kill myself while this wet rag of a girl fights every day to be part of it all. She must be every bit of 13 and has a solid three years of suffering on me. I wish I could swap places and feel my body scrunched and contorted like a teenage hair band—legs so pale and spindly they whispered echoes into the hollow like the long white tubes my Dirty Dancing poster came in. What would it feel like to be stationary? Forcing a stillness where the circumstances of life acted on me rather than through me? Removing choice.

Her feet curve in on one another and overlap like glued feathers. Her bones look weightless and gray. Chalky. Wet on the inside. She moans in a painfully small whimper much like the runt in a litter of puppies I once had—before they all died of Parvo.

I walk by and stop to stare at Nellie. I feel so guilty that I can't stop staring. I freeze as I see the flies go in and out of her mouth and nose. They sit like proud gargoyles guarding the corners of her bluish-gray eyes. I can't help but think they are laying eggs in every orifice. They are taking over her body and maybe that's what is causing her incessant and aching puppy cry. She is begging me, or any person, to stop and just shoo the flies away from her face and put an end to the perpetual fluttering of wings that tickle and taunt her nose, throat, and lungs.

With a heavy heart, I leave with my five-finger discount of Fun Dip. I walk back the way I came, past old Putt-Putt, and sit in my Gram's garden beneath a towering oak tree. The tree feels sturdy. It's my favorite one in her yard because it holds me. The sparkle of the summer sun plays hide and seek through the rustle of emerald leaves and I can't get enough of the fresh-cut grass smell as the shy wind blows. It's a guilty pleasure of mine this time of year. The grass. The Fun Dip.

I begin to daydream about Nellie. The bark of the tree scratches my scrawny back as I fantasize about healing Nellie. Sucking on my Fun Dip stick, I imagine imbuing the lavender powder with magic. I summon the flies to deliver the sacred healing dust to Nellie. I study every fly. They are busy with purpose as they devour the sparkly candy and vomit it on her flesh. They eat their purge and slowly metabolize her disease.

I watch as her whole frailness forms a fly silhouette of buzzing, bile-feeding colonies until she bursts magnificent and translucent wings of her own. Excitement and purpose flood my veins. It's the same feeling I get when I can save a bug from the inevitable fate of a cruel puddle or swimming pool.

I keep the visual going as I begin to pray, perhaps harder than I ever have since I don't believe in God. I pray that Nellie can straighten her feet and rise from her chair. Float. I visualize her neck and spine aligning and stretching tall as she softens her wild, cagey eyes and turns her lip into a smile. She pushes open the old saloon doors with ease, walks outside and into the sunshine, and takes flight.

Sadly, Nellie never flew. She died that summer. Gram told me that she choked on the macaroni her mother fed her for dinner. She was the first person I ever knew who died. Rumors floated through town that her death was on purpose—a homicide; macaroni in the first degree. I even heard a rumor that Putt-Putt Perry did it, but I knew that wasn't true. He was just misunderstood. I wasn't sure what to believe or who to blame—if anyone. Part of me blamed her whistling Dixie mother for bringing her to work every day and putting her on display like a window pet up for adoption. Part of me blamed the black soldier flies that consumed her frail body by orchestrating unspeakable colonies and dusting her organs with eggs too innumerable to fathom. But the rest of me blamed myself because not once did I ever smile at her. Not once did I swat those flies away. I just watched like everyone else.

Ten years later I was lunching with my mom at a café when a young handicapped girl was wheeled in. "Mom, do you remember that time I went to see Gram, and I was obsessed with that little fly girl?"

Taking a bite of her Reuben, she wiped her mouth and replied, "Oh, your cousin, Nellie?"

- **Candice Rankin**

The Artist Hungers for that Elusive Nod

we
are made
of stardust
& connections   each
                    shaped
                    by ancestral
                    divination
artists, every one,
the homemaker, the hunter, the farmer, the baker,
the scientist, poet, philosopher & creator

we, who in making   our art
                         do not seek
                         money, fame or
                         publication
starved for that elusive nod
from another who sees us—really sees us
the one who's tasted, savored, and gorged
on our art and can
turn to us and say   *I see you*
                         I *see you because in your art*
                         I saw myself
the most intimate of gestures from one
to another that solidifies a singular truth
that solidifies a cosmic eternal certainty
airbrushed across universe & millennia
                         that we
                         are made
                         of stardust
                         & connections

- **Anyély Gómez-Dickerson**

Social Studies

I was at the party hoping to meet my girlfriend. That is to say, I didn't have a girl-friend but I was hoping to meet a girl at the party who would be my girlfriend. A girl who would come up to me and say, "You think I'm very attractive, way out of your league, so I'm making the first move. How about we go to my place?" I had a theory that the way to make this happen was to appear aloof. So far, after hundreds of parties that I'd attended over the years, it was still only a theory.

I leaned against the wall next to the bathroom, a high traffic area at a party, serving beer, hoping to catch someone's eye. I was on my third beer, so I had my foot against the wall in what I thought was a casual, "I don't really care I'm just standing here being cool" pose.

An attractive young woman walked up to me and looked me straight in the eye. I nodded to her, thinking, Thank you, God. She stared at me for a few seconds then looked down at my foot on the wall, then back at me. I could feel the heat of her face on mine, that's how close she was. Then she moved even closer. Her eyes were big and brown, and as she gazed into mine, I was hoping she would say something about my long lashes. I've been told they're my best feature. She looked down again at my foot on the wall, but still didn't say anything, so I tried my standard opening.

"Hi," I said. "This is a great apartment for a party."

"I know," she said. "Sherry really wanted her 21rst birthday to be special."

"Nice of her to throw the party," I said. "She's a great kid. I met her in my writing class."

"Oh, you're a writer?"

"Actually, I'm an engineering major, but who knows, maybe I've got the next great American novel in me."

She paused for a second, perhaps to admire my confidence. "I'm Tanya, Sherry's roommate," she said with the hint of a smile.

"Oh, so it's your party, too?" I asked, deliberately withholding my name so as to remain aloof.

"No," she answered, "but... it's my apartment, too. So you want to take your fucking foot off my wall?"

I did so quickly, but maybe not quickly enough for Tanya. She stepped back, turned, and disappeared into the crowd without so much as a "thank you" for removing my foot from her wall.

Sometimes I don't understand girls. I really thought we had something going.

- **Arthur Bell**

Gutted

I was raped, but I'm okay, she says,
hoping someone will call her mom, call the cops,

put her in group therapy, refill her long-
lapsed Prozac script. But everyone has their

own black hole to attend to: a shitty boyfriend,
cancer, car wreck, not enough iron in their diet.

The depths are deeper than they've been in a long
time, she says, hoping for someone to rub her low

back in tiny circles, play music meant for crying,
maybe even just give her a hug. A cigarette

at the very least. But there's too much to do:
bottles to wash, milk encrusted nipples,

the hiss and snarl of boiling water.
Has anybody reminded her about the storms?

Or do we not talk of them anymore? The way
they rattle-tattle your nerves, skin you almost

alive, make it so your mouth is moving
but only moths fly out. While Noah's not-great

grandsons took to the streets, filled the gutters
with blood, we rushed to build arks, I swear.

I just forgot to grab the bottled water and
rubbing alcohol (I always knew I'd be shit

in an apocalypse) so we had to use spit to clean
all the wounds, arrange our eyebrows in worry.

Until our ovaries up and turned to fur. Spidered
away. *Poof!* There was so much rain

that we couldn't see where they went,
so we bid them *adieu,* xoxo, *see ya soon,*

big baboon, hoping that we'd never ever
see them again. Because storms with lady

names are so much deadlier than the ones
named after saints, we figured they were toast.

Because there's nowhere to go but to just
keep going, we knew that we could live without.

I'm so drunk, I can barely walk, she says—sliding
down the wall, her shoes in her hands—

hoping someone will lift her up, take the bottle
away, make sure there are no sharps within reach

because her veins have always been too close
to the surface of her skin because the surface

of her skin has always been too close to her veins.

- Tiffany Promise

Song for Ronit

"I have to pull out weeds," she said,
"Wherever I go," and bent to tug
at chickweed in her mother's garden.
One son in England, military dropout,
has no stomach for state violence
and no future in the land of Israel;
the other studies Arabic, intent
on army intelligence, control.

She would weed her nation if she could,
tug at hatred fueling settlers' hearts;
dig out long tap roots of fear
toward those who cultivated olives
centuries before her people came.
She would pluck out invasive plants
pulling down homes of mothers
who never wanted martyr sons.

The papers talk of transfer and laud
the wall snaking further every day.
Ronit bends down to pull another weed,
until she has a noxious handful
and can heap stems into a great pile
to throw upon the world's waste dump
where poisonous seeds will burn.
"I need to pull out weeds," she said,
            "Always."

- Janet Powers

Underdog

You throw a firecracker bomb
into my hole;
the smoke suffocates me,
leaving me to die underneath your feet.
I have never exposed
my furry brown head to you,
but you know I exist beneath
the earth by the telltale mounds
scattered across your yard.

I need the roots of your flowers
and plants to fill my tiny stomach;
I promise I won't eat much.

Do you realize I am your predecessor?
We are the little mammals
that survived that cataclysmic meteor,
the one that wiped out those
gigantic beasts that once stomped
upon the earth.

So, please, have some respect
before you bomb our villages.
Remember, you were not yet walking the earth
when we first emerged from our burrows,
those early shelters that protected us
from catastrophe.

You are now the great beasts
that stomp upon the earth,
that rule dominion over our
underground kingdoms.

We humbly ask for compassion
for we have as much right to be here
as you believe you do and
you can always plant more flowers.

- **D. Marie Fitzgerald**

Ritual

Les Demoiselles d'Avignon
Pablo Picasso, 1907
The Museum of Modern Art, New York

We've forced our way in, intruded on them
in a dressing room or harem or brothel
in various degrees of nakedness.

Two stare at us, startled but passive;
two others, masked, try to do something:
open a curtain, raise an alarm.

It's the seated one, her body
wrenched around to glare at us
through a mask of rage,
who will do the exorcism.

She'll sever our balls
with an ivory-and-silver knife,
wash them in a river at flood
until they are bloodless and pale,

consecrate them to a terrible goddess
by braising them over hot coals
for all women who ever lived.

- **John Palen**

You Spelled Carrot Wrong

All was not well at Hawk Eyed Advertising. For the fifth time this month, Gillian Parker watched someone walk out of the small office in the back in tears. It was the room where extra chairs and discarded computer parts were stored. It was also the place they took you when you were about to lose your job. This time it was Alice out of accounting, a quiet, nice woman that had burnt something in the microwave last week. It had smoked up the office so bad everyone got sent home for the afternoon. Likely that wasn't the reason she had been let go, but stranger things had happened at the company.

Lauren Leonetti, Gillian's direct boss, and CEO Roberta Watson left the room shaking their heads. Their faces were dressed in pity as if it was the most unfortunate but necessary thing to have happened that day. Everyone else in the office watched them in suspended animation. No one typed, no one scratched a pen across paper, and no one moved a muscle. Gillian tried to focus on her work - the Planet Sparkle presentation that could make the difference between whether or not she had a job by the end of the week - but she couldn't pull her eyes away from watching the pair exchange a quiet conversation. Were they plotting the next firing? Or discussing client strategy? None of them could know for certain. They could only watch and theorize between themselves. It wasn't until the printer erupted and spit out reams of paper that the hypnosis ended. Lauren scurried back to her desk, while Roberta stomped across the room. The normal sounds of the workday started up again and Gillian focused back on the presentation.

"How's everyone doing?" Roberta said, her voice projecting across the room. She smiled and her white teeth gleamed like a shark having eaten its kill for the day. She made a point of making eye contact with each of them as she passed, including Gillian, who squirmed under the brief glance like a prisoner being watched by a warden.

"I'm hearing some carot things!" Roberta continued as she circled the room. Finally, she returned to her office and closed the door. An audible sigh was heard across the office.

Carot things? Gillian repeated to herself. She had heard and seen bizarre behavior before from Roberta that somehow made sense to everyone else. It was all part of working at the large marketing agency that boasted about its ability to stay ahead of the trends. Just a few months ago, without any reason or explanation, Roberta demanded the cubicle walls be torn down and instructed everyone to work side-by-side on their laptops at a large conference table set up in the middle of the room. It was supposed to build a sense of camaraderie and lasted about a week until she changed her mind. She said it looked too much like a school cafeteria. Except Roberta shared a professional shot of the temporary workspace design to Instagram and it was spotted by an editor from Architectural Design magazine. She even won an award for it and it was now part of a burgeoning trend of communal open office designs. Next month they were bringing the table back for a photoshoot done by someone from the magazine.

"You did carot on that presentation, Parker," Mike Davis said, pausing at Gillian's desk and sipping his coffee out of his college sports mug. He was a stocky guy that bragged about his college football career with clients and called everyone by their last name as if he were a coach. He insisted it built camaraderie. It irritated Gillian, but Roberta loved it. He was less intimidating than her other bosses, so she tolerated him a bit more. If only she could ignore his obsession with sports and imitating Roberta's footsteps. "There are some edits you can work on next."

"Working on those now," Gillian said as Mike walked away from her desk and into the breakroom. Reading over the presentation, some changes were minor, while others required inventive rewriting so the client didn't think they were spending too much money. Planet Sparkle was one of the most important clients for the company and probably the reason she still had her job. For now anyway. In the next few months, 15 teeth whitening walk-in clinics would open up across the United States and it was up to Gillian's department to convince the client to spend a lot of money to promote the clinics.

Reviewing the document was a familiar task and one of the elements about her job she liked. She was always good with numbers and embraced analysis like a duck to water. Graphs were her comfort zone. Just last week, Mike had given her the responsibility to recommend changes based on results for their online dating client and it earned her a verbal gold star from Laura. Gillian was embarrassed to think how much the approval meant to her. Yet, it was the reason she couldn't let go of that word. Being in the know was everything at this place. If she didn't embrace the trends so easily understood by everyone else, she became like stagnant water and could be transferred to the "special projects" department where careers went to die.

"Mike," she asked, as he passed by her desk from the kitchen. "What does 'carot' mean?"

Mike tossed his head back, laughing his deep, office-filling bellow of a laugh, and snorted twice. Gillian scowled, regretting her question immediately. It was like high school all over again, and suddenly she had a desperate urge to take back what she said. To pretend she knew all along. She was foolish to reveal what she didn't know, especially to him.

"You're too much, Gillian. How can you not know that word?"

"Carrot as in vegetable?" Gillian started getting warm. The last thing she wanted him to think was that she didn't understand a new word invented by Roberta. Even one as ridiculous as this one. More than that, like a complex math

50

problem, she wanted to figure out the formula to these trends Roberta created. They were stupid, foolish, and short-lived, but effective. Gillian was convinced she could figure out how it happened.

He chuckled, shaking his head. "It's carot. Spelled with one 'r.'"

"Carot...but with one 'r'?" Gillian repeated. "What does it even mean?"

Mike snorted again and walked to his desk. "Figure it out, Parker!"

Frustrated, Gillian wondered who could be safe to ask. She surveyed the open office. Even though their desks were back in place, the cubicle walls never returned, and since she sat in the back of the room, she had front row seats to office politics. Unfortunately, she also sat by the kitchen and bathrooms, which meant everyone going by commented to her about the taste of the coffee, the strange smell in the fridge, or the wait times for the bathroom.

In front of Gillian was Catherine, a bright busy body who spent far too much time on social media than seemed reasonable. Even though it was encouraged for everyone to stay in touch with the trends, Catherine took the suggestion to an extreme degree. She spent the bulk of her time pinning wedding ideas to her Pinterest board. Lately, she was deciding how many bridesmaids she wanted and according to her most recent phone call, the maid of honor was still in question.

"Hey, Catherine?" Gillian asked.

"What's up?" Catherine asked. She minimized Pinterest, brought up Outlook, and turned around to face Gillian.

"Have you ever heard of anyone using the word carot before today?"

Her face brightened. "I love that word! Roberta uses it all the time."

"But what does it mean?" Gillian asked, hoping for a clear answer.

"You know..." Catherine looked up to the ceiling and motioned with her hands as if trying to gather her thoughts. "It means, you know, something really good."

"Hm, thanks," Gillian said, unsatisfied. It couldn't be as simple as that, she reasoned. The word had to be more sophisticated. A slang word as ridiculous as that one couldn't have caught on so quickly.

She grabbed her coffee cup and headed to the kitchen to get a refill. The break room was a cramped space that she stayed in only as long as it took to prepare her food. The centerpiece of the kitchen was two small tables with one chair each that no one used except for new people on their first day. Usually, they sat with their lunch at the table only once, and then afterward would eat at their desk like the rest of them in the office.

Gillian put her coffee cup down on the counter and brought up her phone to do a quick Google search. She typed out the word "carot" in the search field, but her phone auto-corrected the word to "carrot" instead, bringing up photos of the vegetable. It was probably only a matter of days, maybe even less, before

Google would show the word on their trending topics. She needed to know what it meant before that happened and everyone else on social media understood it but her. She heard footsteps entering the kitchen and put her phone away, determined to search for the word later.

Lauren walked into the room with her eyes focused on her feet. She looked up at Gillian and smiled as she headed towards the fridge. "How are things going with that presentation? Mike came back to you with notes, right?"

"He did!" Gillian filled her mug with coffee that smelled like it had been sitting there for hours. She sipped it to give herself a second and grimaced at the cheap burnt flavor of the coffee. Ever since people started being let go, the quality had gone down. Bulk-sized containers of Folgers were crammed underneath the sink to replace the locally roasted coffee beans they all had been enjoying months ago. "I'll have the presentation ready for the review meeting we're having today."

"Sounds good," Lauren said, as she closed the fridge, holding a small baggie of apple slices. "I've been hearing carot things about you. Keep it up!"

There's that word again. "Thanks!" Gillian said, her mind swirling.

Back at her desk, she tried to focus. She brought up the presentation to finish the remaining edits for the meeting. The comments and editorial remarks included "suggested" changes, which Gillian completed. If not, she risked spending an excessive amount of time defending her reasons to ignore them. It was crucial for her to do well for this project. As she read through the document, every so often, she noticed comments from managers and other senior executives using that word. "Gotta get more carot on this one!" "So CAROT! GREAT JOB!" "Make this a tad more carot."

"What?" Gillian whispered. "No way."

She finished editing the presentation and emailed it to Mike for a final review. Afterward, he would likely send it to her again for a few last-minute changes. This meant another day of overtime, but if it saved her job, it was worth it. Gillian noticed Mike, Lauren, and a few others on the Planet Sparkle client team make motions to get up from their desk to head down to the review meeting. Her heart fluttered with nerves as she grabbed her notebook to head downstairs. If she made it through this week, it would be a miracle.

~ ~ ~

Everyone on the Planet Sparkle team gathered inside the large conference room. Glass windows overlooked the downtown area, giving Gillian a glimpse of the partly sunny weather glimmering through the clouds. In addition to the 15 people that worked on the account - all plucked from a variety of departments that rarely came together except for major client meetings - several department heads also gathered in the room. No one would ever say out loud that if they lost this client that would mean their jobs, but the thought hung in the air like humidity before a summer thunderstorm.

Gillian perched on a tall stool in the back of the room. Comfortable chairs surrounded the oversized conference table, but only management sat in those coveted seats. Others followed suit as well. Junior staff and interns sat in the back. It was only last month that Mike claimed one of the comfortable chairs, the one previously occupied by a manager who lost his job after disagreeing with one of Roberta's visions. Everyone acted as if Roberta never had bad ideas, but despite how brilliant her trends could be, a few of them actually cost the company their clients. Recently, her brilliant idea that their chain restaurant client delete their social media to get ahead of the digital detox movement resulted in a ten million dollar loss to the client. Needless to say, they left the agency.

When the last remaining person crammed in, Lauren stood and grinned at everyone. "Thank you all for coming. Let's talk about Planet Sparkle."

Lauren launched the presentation, and the meeting began. Over the next hour, the executives reviewed the material and Mike did a dry run of the presentation, even alluding to Gillian's involvement. The rare kudos gave her a much-needed boost in confidence.

That's when she noticed a few executives giving her nods of approval. *Could it be? Recognition in the company?* Finally, her work was paying off. Then she saw it. One executive mouthed that word. *Carot.* As if a gong had been rung inside of her mind, Gillian tuned out the rest of the meeting. *How did they embrace that slang so fast?* she wondered.

"Alright, that concludes our meeting everyone. I feel really confident about our client presentation tomorrow. Remember one thing: let's be careful here. They are traditional and not quick to embrace new trends. So keep that in mind. This is a big one."

Finally, the meeting was over and everyone filed out all at once. Gillian returned to her desk, more unsatisfied than ever.

"Have a good evening!" Lauren said loudly. She was one of the few managers who left before seven, but made up for it by being the first to show up in the morning. As her shoes echoed her departure, Gillian noticed a folder on her desk. She flipped it open and inside was a birthday card. The yellow sticky note inside indicated it was for Erin in the payroll department. Gillian read over the birthday wishes, and amidst comments like "Happy Birthday" and "Drinks on me," she saw a few others like, "You're so carot LOL" and "Make it a carot birthday."

"You have to be kidding me," Gillian whispered. She scribbled out "happy birthday" then flopped the folder onto Catherine's desk. She walked into the kitchen to grab her lunch bag out of the fridge to have her last snack. As she turned to leave, a manager came in the room. He was one of the nicer ones she only saw in meetings for difficult clients. She wondered what he thought of the slang, certain he would be reasonable. Someone at this company would have the sanity of knowing the foolishness of this word.

"How are you doing today?" he asked, his voice as loud as a mall Santa. He went over to the sink and rinsed out a plate.

Gillian smiled as best she could. "Good, good. How are you?"

He turned off the water and faced Gillian. As he dried off his plate, his smile grew wider and wider. "You know, I feel kind of carot today." He guffawed and slapped his knee. "I love that word." He left the kitchen laughing. His voice carried down into her eardrum, reverberating against the walls of her brain like a pinball machine.

Gillian went back to her desk, eager to leave and let go of that maddening word. She scanned her email one more time before she packed up to go and noticed an incoming one from Mike. As she expected, it was their presentation for the next day and Gillian would make the final edits.

"Hey, did you get my email?" Mike stopping by her desk.
"I did!" Gillian's mind was racing. She couldn't let a stupid word get to her like this. *Let it go,* she coached herself. *Focus back on your work.*

"Great! You can finish it tonight, right?" he asked.

Wordlessly, Gillian nodded. Her mouth felt dry. She opened up the presentation and recognized the same material she had read over about 20 times already. Graphs decorated the presentation, displaying the client's projected growth if they spent a specific amount of money. Under a slide describing one of Planet Sparkle's potential customers, Gillian spotted that word. Mike edited the copy to say the customer will love to see their carot smile. She remembered Lauren's warning about being careful with this client. Then there was that restaurant client they lost, all because of one of Roberta's ideas that almost destroyed their business. *There's no way that the client will know what he's saying.*

Gillian noticed Mike turn off his computer. He grabbed a shopping bag by his desk and walked over. "Everything look good?"

Why did you use that word? Gillian wanted to ask. "Fine. Looks great."

"Awesome. I got to leave. If you want to send that presentation over to Lauren, you can. She'll get it set up for the client tomorrow."

"Okay, will do."

"You did great work on this, Gillian. Management noticed."

Gillian beamed, almost forgetting about the word carot momentarily. *Recognition. Finally.* "Thanks, Mike, I appreciate that."

Mike walked away, heading towards the stairwell, leaving Gillian alone with the presentation. She hit the save button. All she had to do was send it. *That word. I can't leave that word. The client will think we're insane.* The words of Lauren rung in her mind. Maybe it was an indirect request to keep these foolish trends out of the presentation. No one had the gall to tell Roberta when her ideas were stupid, and when they did, they lost their job. Everyone just went along. This was like the emporer's new clothes and they were about to walk into that client meeting naked. It was time for someone to do something about it. It had to be her. Hesitating for only a second, Gillian deleted the word. She put "dazzling" in the place of "carot." *Now Planet Sparkle's customers will love showing off their dazzling smile. Not their carot smile,* Gillian thought. She hit save and attached the presentation to an email to Lauren and her other team members.

As she went home, she couldn't help but wonder if she had made a fatal mistake in her career.

~~~

That night Gillian dreamed about carrots. In her dream, she walked into the kitch-en, opened up the refrigerator, and carrots poured out. Thousands spilled onto the floor. Each one had something missing. One small thing that she couldn't figure out. The carrots filled the room to the ceiling and covered her from head to toe. They jabbed into her waist, poked her in the eye, and punched her in the nose. Then the carrots made their way inside her mouth and down her throat.

~~~

The next day was the client presentation. The office buzzed with excitement as everyone waited for the meeting to begin. Even other departments were excited. Gillian dressed in her Ann Taylor skirt and a white blouse, fresh from the cleaners. That morning, she even took the time to style her hair and put on a little makeup. She was waiting at her desk for the meeting to begin, but when she spotted Lau-ren heading towards her, she knew something was wrong.

"Can we chat briefly before the meeting, Gillian?" Lauren asked with a tight smile. Gillian's stomach tightened. Her boss never stopped by anyone's desk before client meetings. She reminded herself that she didn't need to be so terrified of her boss, but she still felt 12 years old.

"Sure," Gillian said, following her down the hall. They were going into that small meeting room where people get let go. Naively, she hoped that maybe Lauren just wanted to encourage her.

Once she sat down, her boss took the seat across from her. "First, I want to say how much I appreciate your work with Planet Sparkle."

"Thank you, I am honored to–"

Lauren held up her hand, interrupting her. "It should also go without saying that this Deep down, Gillian knew what it was. The company. How she had changed disappointed to our behavior how stupid carot was and how wrong it sounded in the presentation. Instead she went with denial. "I'm sorry, Lauren. I'm not sure what you are talking about."

"The presentation. You made an edit that no one authorized or reviewed. You took action without thought or consideration of how it may reflect on the company."

Carot. A rush of embarrassment flooded through her. "It was only one word. I thought using carot in the presentation was the wrong move. You said it yourself, the client doesn't embrace new trends," she explained, desperate for Lauren to see the word for what it was: a bad idea.

Lauren balked. "Foolish? It was Roberta's suggestion we add this word. You know how invaluable her insights are to the success of our clients." She shook her head in disappointment. "I'm sorry to have to do this, Gillian. But I will have to let you go."

Think fast. "But wait, Lauren." Her mind raced to think of a reason she replaced that word. "But hasn't Roberta heard of the newest word? I'm surprised she hasn't. I've heard it a few times already this morning."

Lauren narrowed her eyes, waiting for Gillian to continue.

"It's...it's...dazzling. But I think I spelled it wrong because it's really spelled with one z and an apostrophe. Like daz'ling."

Her boss searched Gillian's face, looking for the lie. "I haven't heard of that one."

Gillian feigned shock. "You haven't? Really, I think Roberta needs to know. It's a trend she'll really want to get ahead of." *I couldn't have pulled this off. There's no way they'll believe me.*

Lauren glanced at the clock in the corner of the room. "Wait here." When her boss left the room, Gillian tried to breathe deeply to slow down her racing heart. She wondered if they let her go if she would even be able to find another job in advertising.

When Lauren returned, Roberta walked into the small office right be-hind her. The energy in the room shifted to an intense, uptight level that could only be attributed to Roberta. The CEO was dressed low-key in a grey and white-striped wrinkle-free suit that likely cost about a month's worth of Gillian's salary. Lauren's face was like stone.

"Daz'ling?" Roberta repeated, doubt in her tone. Gillian nodded, her tongue stuck to the roof of her mouth. *Act like you know what you're talking about,* she told herself.

Roberta stared down at the floor, leaving the three of them in silence. Gillian hadn't eaten that morning and hoped her stomach didn't make a noise. Sweat populated her forehead but she refused to wipe it away. A bee could land on her face and she wouldn't move. A few people walked by the office, most she didn't know, except Mike walked past and shock flashed across his face. She avoided his

56

gaze, keeping her attention on Roberta, while Lauren stared as if they exchanged a silent, mental conversation.

Roberta looked at Lauren, her expression unchanged. "I like it. Make sure it's spelled right in the presentation."

Once she left, the CEO smirked. "Good work, Gillian. You still have your job. Now go to that meeting, and *daz'le* them."

"Thank you," Gillian said, smiling in disbelief. She stood up to go downstairs and her knees were weak and wobbly, barely able to hold her upright.

"Next time though?" Roberta called out as Gillian left the room. "Don't invent new words without me knowing first, okay?"

Later that night, the word daz'ling went viral. The hashtag was trending on Twitter, and Tik Tok videos were uploaded that were quite daz'ling. Planet Sparkle launched their ad campaign with it and planned to launch 10 more teeth-whitening clinics thanks to the success of the campaign. Roberta got the credit, which didn't surprise Gillian, but at least she got to keep her job. Not only that, she got a promotion into the newly created emerging trends department. It was specifically designed to field Roberta's ideas, although no one told her that. Only an elite few had the guts to navigate that landmine, and Gillian was head of the department. She still dreamed of carrots, though, and something – one small, little thing – was always missing in every single one.

- **Nicole Pyles**

Matters of the Heart

She looks upon me from above a door arch in my living room. With dark, glossy eyes and perky ears, she wears a peaceful smile. I walk underneath her on my way to the laundry room and the office. Her gaze warms my hair like sunshine in the spring.

Before I mounted her up there, I held her in my arms, her head resting on my shoulder. I ran my fingers through her soft, smooth fur. Her long lashes brushed on my cheek.

White-tailed, she was my first deer.

Sorrow fills my heart when I think of that day.

My first bullet penetrated her rear when she stepped toward the feeder. She collapsed and sent an immediate, painful cry toward the sky. After a long moment of kicking and twitching, she flipped to lie on her stomach and pulled herself toward the trees with her front legs. Between breaths, her loud howls shook my bones.

Alone in my blind, a hiding box ten feet in the air, I didn't know what to do. Her heart was supposed to stop instantly. But here she was, dragging her body forward one inch at a time.

With trembling fingers, I reloaded my rifle. Sight toward her left shoulder blade, I pulled the trigger. The bullet hit her upper back and shoved her onto the ground. Unbelievably, she rose from the dust and howled again. Without thinking, I reloaded one more time. Bang! She kicked and let out one last, long breath. Her legs stopped moving midair.

During the next hour, all alone, I sat in the blind with her lifeless body underneath me. I didn't look, but I knew she was there, thirty feet from me. Darkness downed and surrounded the box, and the video of her last moment looped in my brain.

What had I done?

When my husband and friend came to fetch me, I felt relieved at the sight of their F-150's headlights approaching from afar.

That night, for "rosy cheeks," my friend cut open the deer's heart, and my husband painted my face with her blood. The tradition is a variation of blooding, a ritual that traces back to the 700s A.D., as a tribute to St. Hubert, the Christian patron saint of hunters. Huddled around the campfire, we drank our favorite drinks and told hunting tales.

The heat from the flickering flames dried the blood on my face. Toasting after toasting, and laughter after laughter. Warmth ran through my veins, and life filled my chest. The fire's crackling sound whispered in my ears: these are matters of the heart.

We spent the following five evenings processing her at home. Sirloin cubed, shanks sawed, and meat ground and fed into sausage casings. Holding her shattered hipbone in my hand, I understood how I caused her the tremendous pain. I should have waited for her to move into a better position.

Half a year later, the taxidermist readied her head mount.

"You know most people only mount bucks, right?" He asked when I picked her up from his office.

"She's my first," I said.

Thumbs up, he gave me a wink.

Since then, she's observed me every day from my wall. She watches me eat her meat, feed her bone broth to my dog, and drape her pelt on the back of my couch. She knows and I know that I didn't waste any part of her. She knows I did no evil.

Sometimes I look up into her glossy eyes and wonder what she sees in me. What kind of person has her body nurtured?

She didn't sacrifice or volunteer her life. I took it. It was not a small thing and cannot be undone. She was a being, and so am I. But I have consumed her, and she has become part of me. She made me strong. Yet I couldn't give her a quick ending. Because the impatient me didn't wait for a better shot, the greedy me couldn't let the chance go, and the incompetent me flinched on the trigger.

Patience is key in hunting. It is a hunter's responsibility to pay the ultimate respect to the animal by delivering a clean kill. From now on, I strive to be a better hunter and avoid causing the animals to suffer.

Life requires death. We belong to different hierarchies of the food chain. A law of nature. Wolves prey upon sheep, birds eat worms, and humans hunt. Say it's an instinctual act, say it involves humanity, and it is, it's all of that. Call it a reality, drown it with controversies, and govern it with contemporary notions about morality. It's not what we do, but who we are.

I have participated in this ancient, ancestorial practice, though some may deem as barbarian. But I do not hunt for the sake of killing. I am as cruel as one may be to the chicken on the fancy restaurant's menu on Valentine's Day.

As Vilhjalmur Stefansson, the arctic explorer, explained in early 20th century, which Steven Rinella, a conservationist, cited in his documentary *Stars in the Sky*, that the Canadian Inuit hunters had wishes for the bears when they humped the bears' heads out of the woods and mounted them on the wall of their homes. I have similar hope for my deer. In her mystical after-life, when she talks to other deer, I hope she says, "If you're going to get killed by someone, this one is a good choice. Because she's an honorable gal."

- **Marissa Tian**

Postmortem

-on Elizabeth Murray's Tangled
(1989-90)

What happens to a heart that lives a hundred years?
At the autopsy, the pathologist lovingly dissects it
from the body, finds that long ago it was punctured,
yet kept pumping—

To the body entire, the pain
must have seemed nearly unsurvivable, but
the broken vessels healed at the tear and fed it,
and very little scar tissue formed, and it was as if
the puncture was there all along.

At its final beat, the organ burst open at the top,
so that now it seems a deranged lily, an alien womb
that might have held a hundred progeny or more;
so black-blooded is the organ that anything born from it
would be some new species, a superbeing
made wise with the accumulation of a century of memory
and powerful by ingesting whatever vascular miracle
happened there, or an abomination spawned by the merge
of flora, fauna, and some invader, so fantastic
and foreign to the heart as to explode it upon being born.

And at that creature's birth, the dying heart's aortic artery
gushed life out into the body's cavities until
all its blood was spent, and along the jagged edges
of the newly torn tissue,
the flesh of the enlightened organ
went white with relief.

- **Casey Ford**

Meeting the Creator

I must look especially hobbled tonight.
At the sight of me, an Indian man—walking with his wife and her old mother—
stops.
"Do you need help?" he asks.
"No," I say, "I'm just switching off my walking sticks, right to left, left to right."
"Are you sure? I can help."
"I'm okay," I say, "but thank you."

A black woman, as dark and mysterious as the night, walks toward me.
Her welcoming eyes draw me in.
"What a beautiful night," I say.
"Why, thank you!" she answers, as we pass each other by.

It's okay she misunderstood me.
I tell a friend about her reaction.
"You never know," he says. "Might've been the creator in disguise."
"What disguise?" I say. "That's exactly how I imagine the creator."

- Jim Ross

Virtual Victoria

"I want to be an actress," whispered the low, male voice on my phone. "Meantime, I'm a night stocker at the Tenderloin Gap and I'm going crazy."

Born a boy to a conservative family, the voice elaborated, "I left my penis, my parents, and my name behind in Manila last year."

Living a very lonely life under the aspirational identity of Rachel, she'd started hormones and her life anew in San Francisco. But in acting classes there she said she felt marginalized and miscast in classic plays by a teacher with old school limits. Half-minted between hormones, surgeries, sexes, jobs, and citizenships, flooded with desire and faith, Rachel found me online and had a hunch I might help.

I searched my Russian-Jewish cisgender soul hard. I knew the challenge of transitioning, if not by her brave and radical measures. Aging out of ingenue to a character actor to an acting coach and writer, I knew the challenge of giving up old norms, of awakening new skills, of wanting to shed a style of self to survive.

I arranged a first meeting on Zoom with this good-looking, mannered young man and plunged right in.

"Well, first lesson, we all call ourselves actors now," I said. "Not because of any feminist policy, but because 'to act' is a verb, just like 'to teach.' So I don't call myself a 'teachtress' or 'writress' or an 'actress.' Just a teacher, a writer and an actor."

"Okay. Make me an actor, who's going to be a real woman who can play women."

"This'll be hard work. I've got no magic wand," I said. I talked, candid and cautious, about her range. At this phase, she presented as too effeminate to play a straight man and too melodramatic for a naturalistic performance as a woman.

"I'll look for some interim roles. I can't know if your artistic growth will be linear, or that your evolution will be predictable. Let's just trust the process. When you prepare, don't think about how the role should look or sound, just feel how it feels to be a human self with human feelings in different stories, whatever the gender, whatever you wear, however you have your hair, okay?."

"I'm gonna be good, you'll see. This means everything to me."

Impressed with her determination and rawness, I asked for a six-week tryout with homework on roles I'd assign, with Friday online sessions to monitor progress. I felt honored by the responsibility, daunted by the challenge, but very glad to have this focus for us both as a crazy plague erupted in March of 2020. I assigned Albee's *Zoo Story.*

Every week, from inside her parked car, her shared apartment's bathroom, or an office at the Gap, she brought me small slices of her life while deepening the craft I shared from my decades of study and professional practice. Luckily, she fit the first role perfectly and powerfully and I felt optimistic.

As all evidence of a facial beard disappeared, she studied hard to become every new role I assigned. Soon her low voice thinned in a renewed puberty and the flutter of her forced femininity faded. Her pure Filipina soul and a vivid imagination filled each story with palpable intensity, and I had a hunch it could shine through whatever physical personae she'd eventually embody.

Then she shared a play she'd written about saying goodbye to her penis and welcoming a vagina that both scalded and soothed my brain with its pain, poignance, and poetry. I told her it would expand my own vanilla margins to direct her talents in this three-aspect, one-person tour-de-force in progress one day. She fantasized the future and would pray it into existence while I stayed pragmatic about what might be possible when.

Over that year of calibrated hormone treatments, elected surgical procedures, and weekly lessons, she got cast in an edgy new San Francisco play about an "internet cleaner." In her debut as a trans filtering sensationalism and snuff online for web censors, she and the play opened to rave reviews. Sent a filmed scene of one performance, I kvelled. I knew we were on the right track.

I assigned scenes from Pinter, Albee, and McNally, and she dove deeper, no half measures, exploring new forms of herself inside other's stories. And in a changing LBGTQ+ marketplace she expanded everyone's understanding of diverse casting with her flexibility—and mine, too.

In that first year of virtual acting sessions, I nurtured her from innocent chrysalis to a confident Monarch sprouting gorgeous wet wings one year later in Spring of 2021. Then, she missed her session for weeks. Not my place to pursue her, but with pandemic proliferating again, I reached anxiously out. At last, she responded, altered, and not just physically.

"He broke me," she said. Invaginated and fragile, ripe for love, she'd met a masked man at a club who came to court her newborn virginity. New to the wiles of womanhood, she welcomed him too soon to her apartment and her body. Never would've been better. Pinning her down, the suitor cocked his stun gun and raped her, damaged her tender new construction, toppled her scaffolding of faith.

How I wished she were nearby so I could hold her. This pained young maiden could have used some chicken soup and a Jewish mother to make it.

Broken in spirit for awhile, she renewed in name to "Victoria." Now pledged to a good San Francisco church to stay celibate till marriage, she committed ever further to acting. She prayed for roles and for love and told me she also prayed for the salvation of my damned Jewish soul. She soon got cast in a new role as a drag queen Auntie in a new Tenderloin stage comedy about a Filipino family, presented in Tagalog and English.

Another success with good reviews. Tickled by her performance in the filmed scenes she shared, I could feel her power onstage as she practiced for a new life, and even with a small audience in N95's, the applause was standing and huge.

And, defying the gods, overcoming her odds, in the third month of the publicized run, Victoria attracted the love of her life.

Lovelorn cis friends rarely had this kind of luck in love. A stage door Johnny named John came courting and a storybook romance ensued. John's kind Christian family welcomed Victoria as warmly as her family of origin had excommunicated their son now their gifted actor/daughter, cold. They would not invite the couple to visit Manila, nor come to their wedding. Nuptials were planned. She invited me to attend.

I'd never met Victoria in the flesh and had a big hug on hold in my heart for her. I said I would try, depending on conditions. But first, Victoria planned top surgery. She'd implant a bridely bosom in which to embed her brimming heart. Proud that she could finally invest in breasts after a promotion at the Gap, after her first paydays as an actor, she wanted this final touch to fill out her fiancé's mother's donated wedding dress.

No playwright could make up a love story like this, I told her, but if they could, she might write it. "You amaze me."

As her surgery approached, pandemic numbers surged again. I suggested she maybe not rush, that she avoid hospitals and groups of people for the time being, even though this was none of my business as her acting teacher. My boundaries were starting to smear.

"Can you have a small private ceremony now, then have surgery and a celebration later?"

But having held back expressing her heart through a body perceived as male in her young life, she hungered for a pious Christian ceremony within her new congregation, and to offer her refurbished maidenhood for the first time in married love to John.

"I'll take the risk. I know it's God's will for me to be happy."

Thrilled that she would no longer need to strain to look like something she already was, she kept to her plan. She reassured me, prepaid for her next session, would meet me on my screen at our time in two Fridays in full feminine array—a full bosomed bride-to-be, and she'd be a pretty one, I gushed. I assigned her a sexy role to celebrate her upcoming pulchritude.

But when our 55th Friday arrived, she did not confirm, did not show up on my screen. I waited, wondered, worried, texted. She did not answer my messages via Skype, Facetime, or phone. I went down a wormhole of Instagram posts from theater companies, the Facebook pages of photographers, the social media of churches to learn that she had died—"a stroke in mid-surgery" one post said—"instant, irreversible brain damage," said another, "could've happened anywhere, anytime to her," affirmed another.

And now a year past, I still mourn this brave soul I never met, the loving bride she almost became, the actor/playwright she might have been. For me, my student, this ever-evolving spirit has become a miscarried child I could never hold in the flesh, only in my mind and heart, and now in blessed memory.

A woman well loved, an actor of skill and passion, a writer of infinite possibility, I pray she slept deep and left pain-free, thought-free, at that happy edge of consciousness where the wildest most wonderful dreams can come true.

- **Melanie Chartoff**

Wolf Baby

The wolf had been standing at the edge of the woods behind Gretchen's house for some time, partially hidden in the deep shadows between the evergreens. But, Janet thought, that was nothing new or remarkable because wolves often roamed these woods, moving their paws gingerly in and out of the deep snow, searching for some small unfortunate creature to eat. What was strange was that Janet felt as though this particular wolf was watching her. She had put the baby down for its nap and taken a tangerine out onto the back deck where she let the peels fall one at a time, a pile of orange crescents circling her feet. When she had split the fruit into two even halves, she looked up and saw the animal. It was only seven or eight yards from the house, crouched under the heavy branches of a White Pine: its wolfish eyes boring straight through the pale, frigid air.

Janet squeezed the tangerine and watched the juice drip dark tunnels into the snow. She stepped backward towards the door and slid her free hand through the handle, lifting the latch silently and stepping inside. Through the glass, she saw the wolf lose interest in her, turn and walk back into the forest, slipping through the trees as easily as she slipped out of her winter coat. Twice it looked back over its shoulder at her.

The baby slept for a long time and Janet had to go in twice to make sure he was still breathing. She could not seem to get used to the newness of this small creature in her life, the delicacy of his features, the smooth, buttery smell of his skin. He had come unexpectedly, filling her belly with life and longing, kicking her just when she wanted most to sleep, holding still when she most needed to feel less alone. It had been warm still when she stopped being able to wear her pants and normal clothes, tucking more and more of her wardrobe away where she wouldn't have to look at it anymore, wouldn't have to think about the things that were ending and what was about to begin.

After he was born, she couldn't look at him. The nurses held him and whispered to each other, shooting glances in her direction when they thought she was too asleep to see. His eyes glowed like embers in a dying fire: sooty, smoky amber. His tiny body was covered all over with fine soft fuzz, but many babies started their lives that way, one nurse assured her, not looking sure at all, he'd outgrow it, she promised. Not one of them seemed able to look her in the eye.

That night, Janet sat huddled, knees to chin on her hospital bed, in her hospital gown, looking across the room at the cloth bundle in the plastic bassinet. The pale blue receiving blanket was not wrapped tightly enough: one arm, pale and downy, curled up towards the orange heating lamp that warmed his bed. The baby mewled and Janet turned away, pulled the thin hospital sheet up over her head, and went back to sleep.

Days later, alone in Gretchen's kitchen, Janet listened to the baby howling. She had rocked him for what felt like hours, but when he wouldn't stop crying she'd put him back in the wooden drawer Gretchen had given her. When they brought the baby home, Janet had held him in his blankets and watched Gretchen take all of her sweaters out of the bottom drawer of her dresser. She'd heaped them onto the bed, then pulled blankets out of the closet and lined the bottom and sides of the drawer with thick layers of wool and cotton, tucked in tight around the edges so they wouldn't come loose and smother the baby when as he slept. When she was done, Gretchen just looked at Janet and the baby, then at the drawer, and left the two of them alone to work out the details.

The baby's cry had settled into a low wail. If she'd thought he was calling out for her, she'd have gone to him. Instead, she walked from one end of the cabin to the other, counting her steps up and down the long hallway. Twice, while she was waiting for Gretchen to return from her night shift at the hospital, Janet thought she saw eyes peering in from outside, but she must have imagined it, because when she turned on the porch light, there was nothing there, just the trampled snow disappearing into darkness. Still, she locked the doors and windows and tried three times to reach Gretchen at the hospital. It was Saturday night; the ER was busy.

Janet returned to the room she shared with the baby. She stood beside his drawer and looked down at him. Her arms hung dead at her sides as she watched his little face contort with his cries. He didn't stop or even slow down when he noticed her there. His arms and legs pushed and kicked inside the blanket. It seemed too heavy for him, and in that moment—watching her furry baby struggle against the thick wool and the world and her indifference—Janet felt a pang of pity shoot through her stomach. Poor baby, she thought, three weeks old and still no name, no father, no mother. She reached down and touched the top of his head with a finger. Since they'd left the hospital and Gretchen had brought them here, his fur had changed: each strand of hair seemed darker and what had once been baby-fine fuzz now felt thick and bristly. She assumed it was the formula, which boasted four different kinds of vitamin B.

The nurses—Gretchen in particular—had encouraged her to nurse the baby, and she'd considered it briefly, but when they'd brought him to her and the baby opened his mouth, she had seen the glimmer of tiny teeth just beneath his gums and couldn't bring herself to do it. Her breasts had filled with milk, as large and hard as cantaloupes. They were still sore to the touch, but the bottle let her feed the baby from a safer distance. She wondered if breast milk might have prevented the fur, or helped his eyes to turn a deeper brown, like hers.

As she stood there, her fingertips still brushing the top of his head, there came a howl from the window, so loud it was almost right there beside her and Janet yanked her hand back and spun around. But they were alone, and the baby stopped crying. His amber eyes opened, and he looked at her. He looked hungry. Janet backed slowly out of the room.

She left the door open and pulled the ladder down out of the ceiling to climb up into the attic. Halfway up, she heard the glass door on the porch rattle, then shatter, and she flew up the last four steps, tugging the chain to pull the drop-down stairs shut beneath her. The floor in the attic was unfinished and the rough wood scratched her cheek when she lay down to listen.

From inside the ceiling, she heard the wolves move through the house like shadows as they took her baby back with them, through the kitchen and out into the snow. She wondered how they were carrying him. Maybe they used his blanket as a sling, gripping it gently in their iron jaws—just tight enough, but not too tight. Or maybe he was riding on the back of one of the mamas, his fingers wrapped tightly around the fur at the base of her neck, his legs spread wide around her middle.

Janet crouched in the attic until she heard the sound of Gretchen's car, with its clunkclunkclunk that came from deep under the hood somewhere. She heard the key in the lock and Gretchen's gasp at the broken glass. She thought about going down, but there would be a lot of questions. Suspicions. Accusations. She decided to stay in the attic. It was warm there, and dark. She felt comforted by the cave-like walls and the low ceiling.

Men came. The flashing lights glinted between the cracks in the walls and through the dirty panes of the tiny attic windows. Janet stood at a safe distance and watched the men and women searching methodically for her and her baby. Each of them had a flashlight, and each of them had heavy boots, and the boots and the flashlights moved towards the woods like a great stomping army.

They didn't have a chance. Her baby was smarter than all of them and his new family knew how to hide from men. They had caves and fur and small dead animals and all of that is better than heavy boots and a battery-powered flashlight.

When she got tired of waiting for them to give up, Janet lay down in the steamer trunk under the window and pulled an old fur coat up over her body. She closed her eyes and pictured her baby with his new family. He would be so happy there. She knew he would. She only wished she had been able to tell him that she understood. She wanted to tell him that if it weren't for his little amber eyes and his downy brown fur, she would have named him Henry. She would have nursed him and rocked him and sung the same songs to him that her mother had sung to her. She would have taken him to playdates and soccer games and art shows and movies. She would have packed him a sandwich and a snack for school. She would have loved him. And the baby would have liked her, she thought, the baby would have liked her if it weren't for her smooth, hairless skin, her unglowing eyes, her downright normal appetites.

- **Nell McCabe**

68

Snow in August

"Get your feet off the dash," Ari said from the driver's seat of his old 1964 Pontiac GTO which was more rust than its original cherry red. "Haven't you read those crash stories? People's legs get ripped right off."

"And?" Zoe challenged, stretching her legs further up the dash as the two pink plastic hearts tied around the rear-view mirror clacked together. The wind outside tried to steer the car through the steel guardrails and off the mountain. "I'd rather die now, immediately, then slowly over the next three months, Aristotle." She flicked her foot up and down, cheerily, to ABBA's latest song, Dancing Queen, as it fizzled over the car radio.

Ari's hands tightened on the thin steering wheel, his knuckles chalk white. "Don't go Greek on me," he grumbled but went quiet. It bothered him when Zoe brought up her impending doom. It felt wrong to him, knowing the time when someone he loved would die. It once bothered Zoe too, her death, but she'd come to terms with it – or so she'd said.

Through the windshield, past Zoe's flamingo pink socks, the mountain road wound around another rockface. Above them, the midafternoon azure sky hid behind cement gray clouds, looming and heavy, promising snowfall.

"We're close, Ari." Zoe pointed to the clouds, her heels bouncing off the dash in excitement. It was her last wish: to see snowfall one last time. When she told her parents she was leaving their home in the Saskatchewan prairies to drive to the Canadian Rockies, they roared in disapproval, wanting to keep her precious last minutes to themselves. But that wasn't love, spending her time as they saw fit, like dollar bills at the gas station. She called her best friend and neighbour, Ari, and snuck out her window and into the rumbling car he was only supposed to drive to school, and they sped away into the night. Now, twelve hours later and hundreds of kilometers away, Zoe itched for the sky to unleash its storm, her fate suspended within the clouds.

As the car rounded the corner, a lumber truck whizzed by them, too close, too fast. Ari gritted his teeth as the oncoming vehicle forced them closer to the edge, the guardrails screeching an orange cloud of rust.

"We should turn around, Zoe." Ari slowed the car, eager to make a U-turn. "It's getting too stormy up here." He couldn't lose her, not yet.

"But the snow." Panic seized Zoe, making her heart stutter in her chest. If they turned back now, they'd miss the storm, and who knew when the next one would come. She was here now, and time was against her. She knew she'd be dead by the next snowstorm.

But Ari shook his head, his undereyes dark as two purple jellybeans. "It's not worth the risk. We'll find someplace to sleep tonight and try again tomorrow."

"But the storm will be gone by then." Tears streamed down Zoe's cheeks as she realized her last chance was slipping away, like a fistful of sand crumbling between fingers.

Ari noticed the tears, but his throat was raw with emotions as he choked out, "I'm sorry, Zee."

She wanted to fight, to argue with Ari, convince him they needed to push on, just a little further, that the snow would be right around the next bend. But in her gut, she knew he was right. It was one thing to risk her own – shortened – life on this wish, but to ask Ari to do the same, when he'd already helped her get this close to fulfilling her final request, when he had a full life ahead of him, was selfish. Plus, wasn't this what she wanted? Some universal force to determine her fate?

Zoe kept her eyes fixed outside her window, her tangerine headband bright despite the darkness seeping into the sky like ink being spilled across a page. As they traveled down the mountain, she noticed white speckles on her right between the pine trees. Her breath hitched in her throat and it felt like she was hovering inches above the cracked leather seat. It couldn't be.

"Turn right," she shouted at Ari. He didn't respond, focused on following taillights when Zoe reached over, spinning the wheel to the right, leading the car onto a narrow gravel road that disappeared into the trees.

"What the hell, Zoe!" Ari jerked the wheel back, making the car shudder to the left and narrowly avoiding the row of trees, before coming to an abrupt stop.

"Drive," she urged him, "we're gonna miss it."

Ari eyed Zoe as she leaned forward on the edge of her seat, ready to pluck whatever was coming down right out of the sky. He sighed and drove, bouncing down the rough road before they stopped at a mountain outlook. All they could see in front them was the sky, an inky canvas with snow for stars. By any standard, it was a pitiful snowfall, a few flakes falling before melting on the rock outcropping. But for Zoe, it was all she needed.

Zoe scrambled out of the car, whooping and crying. Ari watched her before striding alongside her. She tilted her head back, her long hair falling down her back as the pearly snow kissed her face.

"Why snow?" he asked.

She remained quiet at first, and he thought she didn't hear him, but after a moment, she spoke, "It seemed impossible, snow in August. But look." She motioned to the pitiful falling flakes.

The implications clung to her words; the possibility hung in the air, like the suspended snowflakes. Then Ari understood. This whole adventure, the entire twelve-hour trip, was so Zoe could convince herself this terminal diagnosis wasn't the end, that miracles happen. Snow can fall in August. Zoe can recover.

- **Danielle Guthrie**

Birthday Poem

Next year, for my thirty-fifth birthday, I want pie Instead of cake
Lemon custard, or maybe rhubarb, something different
I want to dance on ice, wear shoes strapped to knives
No stilettos, no makeup
The caterer will serve hard-boiled eggs and raisins, dried ovaries
We will feast in a lush garden, fecund and fertile
where the fruit are not shriveled, rotten, or decaying

Ignoring what is missing, I will shine a spotlight on
the places in my life that bulge and overflow
I am a lionhearted solivagant, decorated athlete, scientist
I will proclaim my existence, celebrate not being dead
embrace the holes in my life knowing that I am whole
This is my fight song

- **Trisha Tavares**

Two Wrongs

Last night—your errant kiss.

After the pre-dinner spritzers, the Chardonnay and Merlot and bloody main course eaten over a table of cream linen and candle glow on silverware, and shortly after the thimblefuls of Port—in the unraveling we do toward saying goodbye—while your wife Rosie lingered in my kitchen fussing her tiramisu into the Tupperware for your trip home, and as my husband Max rinsed suds off his hairy wrists, you, Jonathan, asked where your coat was so I alone would lead you to it. And I did, into the foyer, where your hand on my shoulder stopped and spun me toward you. I lifted my head only enough to address your height: nothing more. What, then, did you misread in the blankness of my face? Shall I tell you what I saw in yours? A man too close to the sun feeling triumphant, an evening's payload of alcohol threading his veins, mistaking the chandelier's flecked light on the wall as some enchanted curtain rendering us invisible. More a lit snow globe in a dark theater, monsters watching. You leaned into me with open lips and clear intent to kiss me hard—your friend's wife. Unsmiling, I pushed you back with a stiff finger on your chin. But behind you, on the far wall of the dining room, the mirror exchanged our images for that of Max, standing in the kitchen, rag in hand, open-mouthed at our reflection. The four of us, forever altered.

The fault is mine, as well. Not for your bad judgment, but for allowing the possibility of it. Roots at their inception cannot always know the fruit they will bear.

At first, our monthly dinners pleased everyone: two couples barely in our forties displaying our evolving tastes in a sophisticated game of house. You and Max, good-sport competitors leaping like salmon up the corporate ladder. Rosie and I, wallpapering your lives with our book clubs, her gardening and volunteer work, my cooking blog and stabs at poetry. That "no-man's" land between the gender trenches, still mostly occupied by women who drive, clean, shop groceries and cook, soft-pedaling careers until the kids are independent. We prattled on while you two talked inside corporate baseball.

I remember how it started. You saw me wince as my husband declared me, in his patronizing way, the "roast whisperer," as though the accolade summed up my life. You began to notice me in the shadow of Max's dominating presence, detecting my hackles. Through some nuance I never intended, you perceived the intimacy lacking in my life. That same evening, as your gentle wife began another slurred oration on the origin of the Pinot she brought, drowning in her passion, your expression thinned to a veneer, behind which lurked a sour disgust.

Two flashlights had found one another in a dark forest. We shared a table only once a month, but it was enough.

You began to unfold to me with stealthy precision. Caught my eyes in a net of understanding while my animated husband monologued to your sweet and besotted wife. Adept at this sort of spy craft, you began to champion my preferences. Pouring my wine without my asking, rising to tug the drapes to keep the sunset from my eyes, sending the bread my way after I merely glanced at it, all while my husband chewed away in oblivion.

Is it not the subtle gestures that make for intimacy?

I was flattered to be seen and understood. A little embarrassed, at first. Contrite even. Then I became intrigued by your desire. Why is it no barrier exists to stop the vapor of thoughts from forming a gravity of their own into stuff that lingers? I confess I started to crave the subtext you offered. I did not echo your glances, or initiate my own. I did not encourage you, but this I admit: for a time, privately, I let your attentions prosper in me. Do you understand how easily a weed can grow in soil left unattended?

But last night you grew bold. "No, let her speak," you said at the table, your finger on Max's elbow after he interrupted me for the third time. I spied the smugness of your expression. Smugness! There's an undertow to desire, Jonathan, an insidious one, that can sting the brain numb.

Over the port in the front room, the four of us inched blindly to the precipice of our true restive selves: your mounting desire to possess me, my husband's radar starting to blip, your wife made simple by booze, and me in paralyzed realization the train cars might unhitch and slide backwards down the mountain. How I wished the evening to end!

My husband lit the fuse. Shushing us to force-listen that Willie Nelson song streaming in the background, the dreamy one about treating his woman second best but now, after it all, he wants her to know it was *she* that was always on his mind. Max closed his eyes in a publicly candid display of his capacity to appreciate the beauty lyrics can illicit, his hands gently conducting the drift of the music.

"A beautiful song of redemption, isn't it?" he asked no one in particular, eyes still shuttered under arched brows.

Oh, please! I thought, remembering the missed dinners, his stale boyish charm arriving late on weeknights after dishes were put away. The on-demand sex. The hollowness in my body as he slept, my eyes wide on the ceiling.

Max's question hardened my face. You saw this, the only other person in the room who really knew the intimate details of Max's life at the office. This knowledge credentialed you in my eyes and you knew this. I wanted to know the truth about Max. And so, for that one time, I opened my mind by giving you a completely direct look. I didn't plead. As you say in your sports parlance, I simply "handled you the ball," the ball that Max was fumbling. Does it surprise you that a quiet, capable woman who so loves poetry could merely flick a switch with her eyes? I regret manipulation of any kind; it's ugly, and the feeling will likely haunt me, but the truth serves no master.

Perhaps you felt deputized to act by your desire for me. Or maybe revealing his hypocrisy in a way only I would understand was a tempting and clever way to continue your quest.

"Redemption? This song is chauvinistic garbage," you declared too loudly. "The singer screws around on this woman for years and now professes to love her, wooing her back with corny words. If he loved her, he would have treated her right in the first place!"

Your double entendre so filled the room with static charge, I couldn't move for fear of an electric arc.

"But I like this song. It's so beautiful," Rosie said. God bless her.

Max kept his eyes closed, his performative hands still keeping time, your words not appearing to blunt him, or so it seemed. You, on the other hand, had fooled yourself, believing the *coup de grâce* had been delivered, that intimating Max's infidelities to me would send me your way. You still believed it fifteen min-utes later under the foyer light.

What did you imagine would happen next, had you kissed me? Did you imagine a passionate tryst in some transient room could replace the open joy true lovers feel exploring the world together? That I would willingly fly from Max's gilded cage to the darkness of yours?

Last night after you left, Max blamed me for your indiscretion, claiming I led you on. I expected this diversion. You see, he would have confronted you before you left but he couldn't risk you further exposing his infidelities, so he laid it on me. Like a fool cursing his shadow. Such has been the price tag for my passivity—so I shed that skin and all that goes with it. The same finger I pushed you away with I held close enough to make him cross-eyed, and I pressed him. He knew what you meant about the song. I unspun his lies, and after much denial, he admitted it all.

We flirt with dreams our entire lives. I protect mine from those who would replace them with lesser ones of their own. I cannot thank you because it was never your intention to free me, but I congratulate you: in the final tally you and my husband are two wrongs that made a right. You opened the door of my cage and crawled in to take my place. I'm leaving him, of course, and, with whatever the lawyers decide, start the catering business I'd always just talked about. I'm leaving you to deal with Max on Monday morning.

- Joseph Manion

Remnants I: Edges

We meet. Bill tells me that he almost called to talk a week before our scheduled session. He says, "I hope that nurse, Lindsay Clancy, dies."

Earlier I'd walked a long way on the beach, taking pictures of consortia— small shore birds, maybe sandpipers, gathered. Dog owners and their cavorting canines.

Alliteration alliteration.

Several surfers sliding toward a promising wave. Fishing people who sat, with long rods poised above them, the nearly invisible monofilament on each, darting sunlight. They watched for a tug; I watched their hopeful tugs.

I see Bill on the screen, suspending disbelief, as is required to maintain the fiction that we can look into one another's eyes, when, really, we each look into our discrete cameras. It's hit and miss, how close to reality you can eye-gaze through a screen. I have a powerful stare, in person. Sometimes deeply empathic; sometimes intrusive or examining, depending on whether someone wants to feel seen, or is projecting onto me some judgment they imagine I have.

I watch and wait to hear what Bill says next instead of saying the many things that come to mind, mostly argumentative.

The tide rushed out from the shore this morning more than it rushed in. The waves did not cover the beach and I try hard not to wash over the silence between Bill's wish that Lindsay Clancy die, and whatever he will say next.

"Because if she wakes from this psychosis, she will start screaming and never stop," he says. Finally. And I don't have an argument against that; just curiosity about how he identifies with her.

Every time we meet, Bill tells me his core story. Rote, and hypnotic, he says, "I never learned anything, can't do anything, and nothing ever works."

I've had no success in nudging him toward a shift in this self-limiting narrative, even slightly. I invite him to think of exceptions--things he has, in fact, learned. Things he's accomplished. The 'somethings' that have worked like his long-term marriage, relationships with lauding adult children and adoring grand-children. I've even waved the toy magic wand I keep next to my chair in the office when we met there, in person, before COVID. We both laugh, sometimes, at my tragic attempt to tug the story-barnacle off the rock.

The only, somewhat convincing exception to his having stalled in boy-hood, occurred during a nine-year stint when he facilitated a self-help group for depressed and anxious people.

"Except for that time, counseling, sort of like you, I feel like an imposter," Bill says.

"You absolutely *were* a counselor. Not like me. Like *you*. You helped people. You still do," I respond. "Everyone in your family comes to you." Still, the man-who-counsels-people is a part of his identity that peels off like a wet sticker.

"At eighty-two, I'm still a boy, *that psychotic boy,* not a man."

Here it comes, the way his story ties into hers. Today, because Lindsay Clancy killed her three children, the little ones to whom she'd devoted her life, he offers himself an ounce of grace for how he'd spent his youth in the interior world of his own psychosis.

Today, because Lindsay Clancy killed her three children, he makes this connection: "By hiding in my interior world, I survived the material one." In the real world, as the last of nine chaotically conceived children, he'd mattered only as errand boy, and as a target for the unruly hands of men.

No wonder he never got taught to tune a car, or seed a lawn, or learn a trade.

There aren't too many ways to remain a boy in a man's body and not feel like an outsider in the world of men. And if you hate all men, then you don't want to be one. Except on behalf of your wife, your children, your grandchildren, the people you counseled who looked up to you, though you're too modest to say "'up'."

To straddle *interior* versus *inferior* reminds me of one of those balance boards. Interior. Inferior. Interior. Inferior.

Rhyming. Rhyming.

Today the sand was spongey, loose, partly wet. Paw prints and footprints penetrated deeply, turning into cups for the wash of tide, and for sunlight and shadow. Walking, sinking, stepping out, my footsteps wouldn't settle, as I have felt unsettled sometimes, before the forces that pack things down have packed things down. We say, "I feel a bit up in the air," or "scattered," or "unbalanced," even "derailed," when we have not yet landed on what makes sense for us.

"If the nurse wakes from this psychosis, she will start screaming and never stop."

Lindsay Clancy committed filicide, in the real world. She strangled her three children. I let my breath seep out, until in a breathless state, for a moment, I feel the emptiness at the depths of Bill's hatred of archetypal MAN. How, if he committed a symbolic filicide of his *interior* boy, no longer shielded in walls of psychosis, it would leave him as what? A self-hating man?

We humans have parts. Body parts. Psychic parts. Sometimes they work together well. Sometimes their coordination goes off. Way off. Some parts claim preferred identification, and some we reject. In our culture, we women have lots of body parts we've sliced off, propped up, plumped, stretched, dyed, injected, and refused to look upon. And we've an equal stash of psychic parts vying for the boardroom--whether vacated or crowded.

This might sound horrifying, but some mothers would give their lives for the children they love, in a forced choice. But they don't *like* being mothers. They might *not* say, "I'm a mom," at an introduction. Instead, "I *have* a child."

The roles that occupy so much of our time, and in which we build great skill, even devotedly, don't always represent who we are. We, like Bill, have interior rooms in which parts of us hide out, go dormant, even die.

Mostly, women all over the world service the needs of others, and of course, their children. To bend into and around this, you must abandon or neglect your other selves, at least somewhat. At worst, mothers lacking privilege, in many countries, may be indentured, enslaved, or savaged into it.

Or, you might be an archetypal MOTHER, as I imagine Lindsay Clancy to be, adoring your children with a passion so great it takes everything from you. The mother archetype celebrates fertility, and rebirth, the creativity of bringing new life into the world. But there is, of course, the dark side of secrecy and hiddenness. The edge. The looming abyss. The world of the dead. A nurturing that can devour. The love that poisons. The psychic valences of this loving, and terrible, mother. The mother who smothers. Who thinks her children can't breathe without her, even as they leave her without breathing room for herself, even as she wants more of them.

A murderous mother can love her children too much. She lives, eats, and breathes them; she feels their pulses in her own veins. In an all-consuming way they are hers, are part of her, are better off dead than without her. She's even eaten their placentas, saved their umbilical cords, or might have.

"If the nurse wakes from this psychosis, she will start screaming and never stop."

According to news reports, Lindsay Clancy is emotional without being emotional. Cannot cry or smile. As numb as anyone might experience, having lived through the unthinkable.

This morning, while walking on the beach, before the tide came in, I found, "I LOVE YOU JENN," written in the sand. Spilled from a heart that could not contain such adoration, they logged it onto the disappearing world. They wanted the 'lie' of forever, to last a bit longer, if not beyond the possible. Love, sometimes so granular—Lindsay Clancy listened to her children's little hearts with her nurse's stethoscope, took their temperatures, dressed them just so, to go outside and build a snowman—can sometimes burden you with an indiscriminate tonnage beyond carrying.

The prosecution will argue for monster-mother, the cold-blooded planner, the strangler, the one who watched as those several agonizing minutes ticked by in the basement of her house and the children died slowly, their breath denied them.

The defense will argue for praiseworthy mother, a mother poisoned by her own post-partum chemistry, plus the added onboarding of medications gone awry, delivered by a medical system that failed her.

Bill hopes Lindsay Clancy won't come out of her psychosis because she won't be able to live. Bill chips away at his own defense against integrating 'boy' and 'man' today. Because, today, the underdeveloped man gives some grace to the boy for hiding out. What now makes some emotional sense, seems less like an inherent fault.

Bill and I laughed today too. He'd mistakenly turned his phone camera around and I said something like, "Your knee is talking to me now, but I can't hear it very well." It felt good to laugh about something silly and real-world. It's difficult to stay on the ocean floor of Bill's world for too long, where the undertow of trauma banished his childhood.

Also, this morning, at the edge of the water, the ocean licked my toes, spit on me, formed foamy arcs, like a kind of lace, and disappeared, loosening my foothold.

Alliteration. Alliteration.

I love words. I love the sounds of words. I love the way they, like the ocean, slip me between this world and that, between Bill's story and Lindsay Clancy's story and my own.

As I've said, we all have parts. Lindsay Clancy's audience, too, will bifurcate, will prosecute, or defend. Some will say filicide has no excuse. Others, particularly those who've spent time in the radiance of Lindsay Clancy's love and devotion, will say that her own deeds have caused her enough suffering.

No one thinks casually about a mother who murders her children. We can wrap our minds around lethal crimes of passion. And, with disgust, we can wrap our minds around cold-blooded murders by psychopaths--whom we view as non-persons. We can understand the cultural narrative of gang members and drug lord's crews who subscribe to a different set of rules about loyalty and merit. But murders of their own children by dissociative mothers prove hardest.

I mean, listen to your own mind. Twenty-four hours a day the chatter goes on. Our vulnerable parts tell us lies. Story wars with story: *I am worthy of the promotion. I'm an imposter who doesn't know what I'm doing. I love my life. I'm bored as hell. I'm so close to him. I don't know who this man is. I want to eat cleanly. Give me the chocolate cake I deserve.*

The better lie doesn't always win. The lie doesn't always seem to come from us. The lying part may take off like a missile, ripping through brain, bone, muscle, and skin. It will camouflage well as something external, until it's not-me completely. Not me at all. Disembodied.

Lindsay Clancy's fate will hinge on the most convincing description of her identity. Loving, crazed mother versus cold murderess. But look at the facts: Her children wake up and she feeds them breakfast. She takes one child to the pediatrician and a prescription gets sent to the pharmacy. She feeds them lunch. She dresses the older ones for winter weather and plays with them in the snow. She chats with her husband and talks to doctors on the phone. She looks up close-by restaurants. She sends her husband to pick up the prescription and the takeout dinner. She suffocates her children in the basement. She jumps out a window.

What train of thought makes sense here? All we can see is a catastrophic uncoupling.

Bill's 'boy' and 'man' keep vying, uncoupled too. At least, today, we have hope that he might create a new image of 'man,' one that his 'boy' might like to embody, someday. Maybe when he's eighty-four or eighty-six?

For my part, I can tell you stories about other people's stories and yet, today, I can't decide if I'm a barefoot beach-walker or a sneakered one. Achilles tendons can tell you there are vast differences.

Coaches for barefoot sand-running tell you to steer clear of slants, of uneven pressures on bipedal ambulation, as if such beaches exist that don't lean into the sea. Runners, or walkers like me, will feel the weight and the torque on one ankle and foot more than the other. We will balance that tug with the hip or shoulder on our other side, with the tilt of the neck toward land. When we turn around to go back the other way, the counter-tensions will shift.

It's the way of the world, no? You lean or reach toward one thing while having to anchor yourself to something else? You don't want to go over the edge, to slide all the way in...to the ocean, to love, to agony?

- **Lisa Friedlander**

Finding Mary

You should never judge a mother whose daughter is in the hospital. Even if she resorts to subtle prostitution or worse to save her child.

I am sitting in front of Prof, in a secluded corner of Portharcourt Sports Club, with my wedding ring safely tucked inside the small zip of my purse. Our legs faintly brush against each other under the table. Whenever I muster the courage to look into his weathered eyes, they are adoring, worshipping. I smoothen the crease on my skirt and whisper to the waiter,

"Water is fine."

Prof clears his throat, and without looking up, I know his mouth is forming a tight thin line.

"Err ... I mean, I'll have whatever he is having." I have no idea what he is having.

So, I look around the club, dotted with people who have too much money and time. A man is teaching his daughter or mistress how to play lawn tennis. I turn to the table and Prof's affixed gaze when the whiff of spiced suya reaches my nostrils.

"What is on your mind, Mary?"

"Prisca is in the hospital," I respond, my hands shaking. The last time I saw her, she had begged us, saying, you people should allow me die, please.

"How much do you need?" He drops his toothpick and wipes his hands on his shorts.

I have never asked him for something this huge. Even as he reaches for his phone, I know he will send something sufficient, superfluous, just like him. Two minutes later, my phone dings.

~ ~ ~

Sutonye's voice fills the hospital corridor, directing me. Bari is asleep on the bed beside his sister, his arm snaked around the teddy bear she is holding. I stand at the door, watching the only people that matter to me, all in one place. Sutonye looks up and motions for me to wait. He places the Ladybird children's book he is holding on the bed, and joins me at the door.

"How far? Wetin Aghalino talk?" he asks. I understand. Pidgin English often attempts to accommodate the width and depth of words we consider too heavy.

"E give me double." I whip out my phone to show him the credit alert.

He takes it and whistles softly. "Omoooo. This Prof sha."

He looks at me all over. I shake my head. "E no touch me. We meet for Portharcourt Sports Club, no be hotel."

He hugs me tight and I hear the beat of his heart against mine. In the rhythmic sound, his heart whispers words too fragile to be spoken, not even in pidgin English, into the delicate white walls of Madonna Teaching Hospital: *Oh, Mary. I wish I had a better job. I hate to push you to Prof I would never forgive myself if he ever tried anything funny with you. I love you so much.*

He kisses my forehead and then leaves to go see the doctor.

~ ~ ~

When I heard about the sex for grade lecturer in Unilag, I called Sutonye and we talked about it, making jokes and asking each other to confess now if we had any lecturer bothering us for sex. We talked about other things a Mary should never say or hear. We talked late into the night and only ended the call because we had a test the following morning. I woke up late, and Professor Aghalino had already entered the class. Which meant nobody else could go in. Sutonye already left three million WhatsApp messages for me:

-babe, where are you? 8:01 a.m.

-you know we will not see this man until exam day...this test is important. 8:02 a.m.

-omo, you're killing me. 8:02 a.m.

-fuck you! 8:05 a.m.

-Mary, e don close door o. 8:05 a.m.

I replied his messages calmly, as I would have if he was standing before me, being dramatic and worried:

-*text me the questions. I'll type and answer from here.*

Thus, I took my History of French Revolution test at a cafe by the school gate.

Sutonye wrote fast and did as I asked, only that he forgot to change his pen or handwriting. Professor Aghalino summoned us to his office the following morning.

"How could you be this stupid, Sutonye Brown? And see, the girl you helped scored more than you did."

"Excuse me, sir. That was because I took the test myself. I just wasn't in the class at that time."

He looked up, as if just realizing I had been beside Sutonye all along.

I showed him the WhatsApp chat, and he went through his records for my previous scores. He eventually looked up from the records and regarded us with an expressionless face.

"That will be all for now," he said.

We left the office, cold and worried. Cold from the air-conditioning, worried, about what to expect from the course- a really good fail or an invitation to face a disciplinary committee on malpractice.

At the beginning of the next semester, Prof called me to his office. He showed me my exam script, with notes and comments detailing my performance: 5 for attendance, 9 and 6 in assessment tests, 59/70 in exams.

Prof became more regular in class, and every time he came to class, he scanned the expanse of the room for me. He asked my opinion on issues from our course readings to submissions his colleagues made for publication or issues related to the university in general.

Perhaps, I was drawn to him because he did not come to me with guile. One afternoon in his office, we were in the middle of a conversation on neoliberalism and Africa's place in current capitalism when he stopped talking abruptly. I shifted in my seat, confused.

"Prof, is everything okay?"

"Mary, I know my place and I probably should not be saying this. But you make me feel things no woman has ever made me feel."

I looked up sharply.

"And no, I am not even talking about sex. Marry me, please. Give me this honor."

I open my mouth to speak but he holds up his hand.

"You don't need to give me an answer now, or even any time soon. Also, whatever your answer is will not tamper with our cordial relationship or your grades in any way. I give you my word on that."

I caught myself thinking about Prof once in a while, and I blamed the Yoruba phenomenon that, the leaves which wrap a bar of soap eventually become one with the soap. I do not know who is the leaf or soap, I just know I *like like* Prof.

On my 25th birthday, he invited me for dinner at Presidential Hotel. In the coolness of the evening and soft laughter, I found myself considering him. Comparing him and Sutonge.

"Do you know what we call you in class?"

"Haha, tell me please. No, don't tell me. Okay, okay, I'm listening." He looked younger than forty-five now, the evening wrapping him in pure innocence and boyish excitement.

I took my time before answering, smiling over the rim of my wineglass. "Uniport Finest."

"Eh?" He threw his head back, laughing like God.

Moments like this, when Prof is just a man and I am just a woman. I want to hold all of him in the cusps of my palms and close him there. Something mine, to love and to cherish.

~ ~ ~

I find myself loving his distinctive personality, which earned me respect and boosted my confidence. His friends never looked down on me or made ribald comments about me. They were always courteous and respectful, as opposed to how they joked about small girls from Uniport who liked free things. Prof made it clear that I was not a small girl in any way.

~ ~ ~

Prisca runs out of her room and dives into the kitchen, almost slipping on the puddle of water her brother had spilled. My right hand flies to my mouth and the other to my chest. I let out a gasp that sounds as though I was being strangled. Sutonye smiles and reclines against the chair.

"Relax. She is fine. The doctor said so. Are you not happy to see her this active? Three weeks ago, she was puking and asking me how to die."

"But...but..what if she hits her head on the ground?"

"Okay," he claps his hands on his thighs and gathers both children in his arms, tickling them each on their necks.

Later, he is moving inside me with the grace of water, whispering things. A sob escapes my lips, and he sinks deeper into me. Another sob, and another, and I roll away from under him.

He knows what is on my mind. He sees how I check my phone every minute to see if my boss at the bookshop has sent my balance. We have used all we had to pay for school fees and stock the house with food. But with each passing day, we have less than we did previously.

"It's okay. If the local government election is successful, my salary will come in at the end of the month."

I spin around, vexed. "With those thugs from Ahoada and Omoku? Will you vote? Nobody will go out to vote anywhere because those boys will flood the streets with guns and cutlasses."

"I'll do menial jobs if I have to. But please, don't worry. The children can tell when you are sad."

I nod and turn back to the bed. He is flaccid now, so he settles beside me, holding me. I close my eyes and open my mind, welcoming thoughts that are beyond me...

I wake up before five the following morning, go to the kitchen first, and then the bathroom, leaving the door slightly ajar. I set to work, first with my face, then with my arms. As I catch my reflection in the mirror, I see a woman who knows she is not well. To make the process easier, I turn the mirror to the wall and tell myself I am one of the few mad women who actually know they are mad but cannot do anything about it.

~ ~ ~

I am running out of patience and blood when Sutonye finally opens the door. His voice jumps at me as a thundering clap, simmered to a horrified whisper.

"WHAT ARE you doing? Jesus, Mary what...wetin be this?" His hands reach out to hold me but only grapple at the air in front of me.

I smile shakily and rush to explain my plan to him. He falls silent for a long time, and in this period, my heart is pounding, begging me to think again before I ruin my life forever.

He asks me to go over the plan again and again.

When he finally takes a calming breath, he retrieves the knife from the tub and gently turns my arms to face him.

"When you want to cut yourself as though someone else has cut you, you have to cut as if you put up a fight at least: with precision and a little distortion here and there. Some cuts will be deep, others, not so deep and some, just a scratch, like this." He cuts slowly as he speaks, his words cutting deeper than any knife. I pinch him hard, to hold back from crying out. He sniffs and wipes tears from his eyes. Bends on one knee and draws a long and ugly slash on my thigh. I slap his back in quick succession, hoping the pepperiness of my slap will give him a faint idea of what I feel.

Blood is everywhere on the bathroom floor. He carries me out carefully and lays me on the bed, applying methylated spirit with cotton wool.

"Because I did this very early in the morning and left you in the house, you cleaned yourself up before going to see him around past 8. Not so?"

I nod.

His tears fall on my nightie as he works.

"What will you tell the children when I leave?" I ask, distracting myself, needing to know.

"I will tell them you got a new job in Port Harcourt and will only come home once in a while. I will tell the neighbors the same thing too."

I hate him for thinking out this part of the plan I had missed. I wish he would pretend to stop me and not be so agreeable to this outrageous idea of mine.

When he is done cleaning me, he helps me pack my bag, carefully selecting clothes and mismatching them. He makes to arrange them in the box, but changes his mind and stuffs them in. Hurriedly.

As he lies beside me on the bed, while we both wait for eight o'clock, I wonder if he has thought this plan and infused it into my head, somehow. If perhaps, I am only doing exactly what he is too ashamed to suggest to me.

~ ~ ~

I get to Prof's house before eight in the morning. Elele is only about 45 minutes drive to Portharcourt, ruling out unforeseen circumstances like fifty police checkpoints, bad roads, traffic and kidnappers. I use a long black veil to cover my back and neck. The man beside me on the bus strains his neck once in a while, trying to peep into whatever he believes I am covering.

When I open the door, Prof is at the dining, taking tea and reading the papers without his glasses.

"That you, Mary? I got your text. What is the urgent thing that came up?"

I drop the veil and open the slit of my gown, waiting for him to look up.

I see him struggling to remain calm. His chest heaves, and he rushes to stand up. "Who did this to you?" His hand goes to his phone, and I know he is already trying to remember what name he used to save the Inspector General of Police's number.

I fall into my new life as a victim, truthful in every aspect of my story,

84

because when I tell him my husband did this, I do not lie.

"What? What? No..no...what?" He holds himself back from meddling in my marriage, yet he feels obliged to do something. I came to him, after all.

I sit and take my time to explain the brutality more, then end it with:

"Prof, he did this mainly because he saw an old text you had sent to me. He was drunk, you know. He kept on saying I was cheating on him with you because he doesn't have money. My children were crying and begging him, and oh God." I bow my head, marveling at how good I am at being mad. I wonder how if there's a limit, now should be a good time for the alarms to be blaring.

My confession ties Prof's hands into a firm knot as he begins to blame himself for my misfortune. His earlier anger and indignation dissolve to regret and pity.

"I swear, I will get your children back, and that boy will rot in jail. I will show..."

"Ah, no please. Don't do anything." I beg, wincing as I go on my knees. I tell him I do not want to put my children through all that. When I run out of reasons, I tell him I feel dizzy, and ask if I could stay with him.

"Of course, of course. Should I get my doctor? Come upstairs and rest." He tucks me in and sits across me.

"Do you need anything, Mary? Anything."

"I feel useless. I am so useless, Prof. I am sure if I had a master's degree and maybe, a better job, Sutonye would treat me with more dignity. A woman is nothing without her pride. What is my pride, Prof? Nothing! Oh God."

I add some more sobs, and Prof comes to my side. He consoles me, then, in a firm voice, says, "I promise you, Mary. You will get all this and more."

"Thank you, thank you. What would I have done without you? Who else do I know in this Portharcourt?"

He smiles, pats me on the shoulder and calls from the door:

"Let me know if you need anything to make you more comfortable here, okay?"

"Yes. Thank you very much, Prof."

"It is fine. You will be fine, Mary. Rest for now."

As he leaves the room, I pull the cover over myself and text Sutonye: Step 1, done and dusted.

~~~

A lot can happen on weekends. Prof is away to see his mother in Bayelsa. I could sit, staring at my phone as I gradually become a millionaire-one credit alert after the other. I could visit Elele to see my husband and children. I could complete my master's degree application process and resume school in a month. My point is, it does not take long for your life to change if you are willing to take risks.

I adjust my suit jacket and grab my briefcase. I roll my traveling bag out of the boot and greet my neighbors who rush to congratulate me because they believe I work in NNPC or SHELL. I know they will soon begin to submit their children's CVs, and I will smile and tell them I will work on it.

Sutonye is not in the house when I return. I pick the key from under the foot mat and head to the kitchen first. The freezer is stuffed with chicken laps, and frozen soups and stew, with the money I regularly send to him. My kitchen has never looked so small, with bags of rice and tubers of yam.

I hear Prisca's squeal from the junction of the house. She runs in, her brother tailing her. Sutonye grins like a new groom. My heart swells with joy as I am rewarded for the sacrifice I make. When the children fall asleep, Sutonye and I talk and make plans. I make more cash transfers to him, and he immediately transfers them to the appropriate channels.

When he moves inside me now, I do not feel the grace of water in his movement. He moves with a fevered urgency, slippery with excitement.

~~~

One Sunday night, Sutonye and I are sitting at the TV, watching a home drama. A woman is married to a man old enough to be her ancestor. She takes money from him and gives to her boyfriend, who in turn gives to his girlfriend, who in turn gives it to her boyfriend, who in turn… a long endless chain of unfaithful lovers, smart and stupid at the same time. We could not see the movie's end because our cable was cut as our subscription expired. But in my mind, the ancestor finds out, and everybody dies.

On Monday, I am back to Prof's place. As I dance about in the kitchen, rustling dinner for Prof and me, I feel that movie's scriptwriter and producer should see me for consultation. I have so much to teach them. I could be the director for the sequel.

Sutonye sends me a picture of the house we are building with Prof's money and I send one back to him of painting designs for the children's rooms. We laugh and send emojis and selfies to each other. He tells me the house will be ready in December, and we need a new plan to evacuate me from Prof's house.

-Guy, it is your turn to think, please.

-haha. We both know you are the smart one. Your brain is always on fire.

-okay, I will come up with something and keep you posted.

Outside, I hear Prof asking me if I have finished the assignment he gave us in class. I tell him I only have to add one or two sources. He jokes about how he has prepared tough questions for my presentation, and I tell him to bring it on.

~~~

My grandmother told me a story of a small village not far from ours in Ekiti state. The villagers never close their doors when they sleep because there's no thief in the village, but if a thief is unfortunate enough to stumble into the small village, they catch him, and each of them, old to young, hit a nail into the center of his head. When they are sated, they release him and let him wander through the night. He cannot go to the hospital because he would have to explain how the nail got into his head. The thief ends up dying anyway, slowly and agonizingly.

When I first heard it, I was livid with anger, asking where their humanity was. If my father had not asked me to shut up and keep quiet, I would have marched to the village to see their king and spit in his face.

Now, I wish I was the village, with so many people and many hands. With a big fat nail and a heavy stone to hit a nail into the center of Sutonye's head and let him go.

~ ~ ~

I have all the signs of pregnancy even though Prof and I never got intimate in that manner, and I never let Sutonye finish inside me since I moved in with Prof.

I walk around the house, trying to replay everything in my head to see where I had gone wrong. I had returned to the house in Elele and met it wide open. Two goats, manning the two-bedroom flat. Our neighbors were kind to direct me to the new house, which should not be ready until December when I would leave the Prof and move in with my family.

Parked a few meters from the house, I think about how this could be a surprise and how if it is, I do not want to mess it up. I start the car and turn to leave. After all, my next visit was supposed to be in two day's time.

My side mirror catches a view and I slow down. A girl who looks like Prisca is holding a woman's hand. A man who looks like Sutonye is carrying a boy who looks like Bari.

Were my eyes blurry with tears when I saw them? Or did I see what my mind wanted me to see? Are children so unstable to trade one mother for another so easily? And why can't I reach Sutonye's line?

~ ~ ~

Prof returns from work and talks about the paper I helped him write. I nod and smile, but not before a few tears fall to the ground. I bend my head, my jaw touching my collar bone. My shoulders turned inward. My cry grows from muffled sobs to blown out wails. More betraying it is that of all people, it is before Prof I finally come undone, piece by piece.

He stands there, not offering a consolation. His hands solemnly folded at his back as he considers me. We remain in this position for as long as I have tears to shed. When I translate to dry heaves, he clears his throat and smiles.

"Do you want to talk about it?"

Can I? The wheels in my brain are stuck in quagmire. They creak and groan as they stop working. What will I tell him? I shake my head and summon hot hears from my crust.

"Men are evilllll." My voice sounds monstrous to my ears.

He comes to stand beside me now and pulls me into the hollow of his arms. "Mary, listen to me now, this thing your husband has done, he is not the first man to do it, and he will not be the last."

I shake my head. Sutonye has not done anything. He has only disappeared. The people I saw in our new house are interlopers, and I should be questioning them now to produce my family.

I stand up immediately and head for the door.

"Come back, Mary. For how long do you want to lie to yourself? Sutonye turned out to be smarter than you in whatever game it is you both were playing."

I fall silent, letting the words attach themselves to my brain. I look up into his eyes and meet a knowing smile.

"Now, are you going to stay with me for real this time around? Will you start afresh again? Or do you want to be the woman who loses in everything?"

"But my children..."

"Do you trust me?"

I nod.

"We will go to court on Monday and do it the right way."

I nod again, wondering whose script I am acting out now. Stretching as required of a woman to fit my new role.

- **Deborah Oluniran**

Mushrooms

She sank, soft, between a beech tree and an oak,
cradled by their roots, her mattress dying nettles
over bramble springs; blinds of bracken split
the wintry sun to slits of light. She slept, alone,
each year tucking her more comfortably
into the forest floor, the spores of mushrooms
settling in her loosening flesh. She dreamt,

remembering his skin, grainy with hairs
like ants against her own; his smell, rank
and sour against the green scent of the trees;
his cruel hands, slapping and scratching,
the stones of knuckles punching a pattern
like hammered silver in her tender shell; then
the knife, glassy in the moonlight. Thoughts

curled about her, murmurs of tree breath,
the snow's soft feathers, the damp earth
reaching for her, sunlight's scrabbling fingers
and midnight's disapproving stare. But the mushrooms
warmed her, yellowish caps like ballerina's skirts, held
stiff by frothy gills, *en pointe,* the finger-tips
of secret messengers, connecting tree to tree. Life

caught her up, a metamorphosis of teeming
fungii, as she dreamt her sluggish dreams, no longer
quick like darting flames that leapt from thought
to thought, but measured and prolonged, like
the gradual greening of the woods in spring,
the slow awakening of the summer sun, the quiet
seething sleep of winter, navigating home.

- **Louise Wilford**

My Goodness, My Darling

I told my daughter last year, "We're starting over, life will be better," but she was eleven and delicate and only heard, "We're moving far away." She cried for a month and told me over and over she wanted to stay, so I let her. Slowly, I packed her broken heart pieces in paper with mine and watched as the house filled with boxes. When it was time, we got in the car and headed south, stopping briefly at her father's doorstep before I continued on alone.

In a short while I was back, another mangled new beginning dragging lifelessly from the bumper. Then winter turned to spring and spring to summer, as they do, and I told her, "I'm starting over again, going back to school. We'll get to vacation together, let's go camping this summer and to Paris when you graduate," but she only heard, "I'm moving far away again," so she cried again and asked when I'd be back.

As I packed up her pieces and my belongings found their boxes, she left a line of breadcrumbs through them: her old favorite book, a wooden box I gave her before she was born, a pocket knife with "Kate" on the handle.

Don't you want these at your dad's?

No, I want you to keep them.

I tried to tell her there's a difference between living somewhere different and leaving, and I'll never leave her. But the waterline beneath her trembling blue eyes brimmed and spilled every time I said, "Oklahoma," because when you're twelve and delicate and have already lost her once, your mother going somewhere different feels a whole lot like leaving.

I told her I'll be back all the time, you'll get to ride airplanes and I'll send you new books. What I wanted to say was, my goodness, my darling, what kind of mother would draw your tears this way even once, then again? I'm sorry. I love you. I'm sorry.

Now, in a half-boxed house, she pulls on a new dress for dinner. The neckline and her collarbones lay fertile for a piece of jewelry I didn't think to buy. I tell her we'll find a necklace tomorrow. She says she doesn't need it.

Brush your hair.

I did.

Let me see.

She rakes her fingers through to prove it until they catch in a fierce tangle halfway down. As she moves to the small bathroom at the back of the house for her brush, I recite our poetry in whispers – *I want you to keep them // Brush your hair // I'm sorry // Let me see.* She hands me the comb like a gift wrapped in paper and wriggles in her half-done dress as I repentantly smooth the knots from her long blonde hair.

Can you zip it?

Of course, stand still.

Gliding the pull tab up between her shoulders, I ask her about a ponytail. She lets me twist her hair in a clip before we take pictures of ourselves in the old bathroom mirror that's propped against the dining room wall.

You take too many pictures.

You can never take too many pictures.

She smiles for me anyway and I wish we could get ready for dinner a while more, but we have to go while her dress is still new and the food is still warm.

A soft summer breeze carries us down the sidewalk toward the candlelit Indian restaurant in Hingetown. Hand in hand, we float past the old stone church and the long brick wall painted like a Chinese dragon. Kate skips over the grass-filled cracks, tugging my arm toward a wrought iron gate, curious about the Little Wooden Library behind it. She looks inside, cocks her head and scrunches her nose.

There are cans of food in there.

I take a picture of her twirling back through the gate, riding the breeze down the aging sidewalk, hair wisping from its twist toward her grandparents on the corner. She chases a butterfly and giggles like I'm staying; soars down the street like she'll grow up here forever.

I'm thinking of a poem I once read that says:

We're all made of birds wings and Van Gogh's ear

a snail shell

the fall of Rome.

Nothing is destroyed, just made into other things. Kate pauses at her reflection in a window pane at the corner of Church and West 28th, and I marvel at all the curiosities, summer breezes and heartbreaks that have made her.

Come on, I tell her, let's go,

but what I mean is,

We're starting over, we can travel.

Lets go to Paris, please don't cry.

And now she's walking down Church Street and I'm watching her go, in her pretty white dress and her long blonde hair, and someone should tell her, I think. Someone should tell her.

I call out, Hey slow down! But my voice feels hot and sharp falling out, because after all those broken heart pieces and boxes and breadcrumbs what I'm really trying to say is,

all you really need to hear is,

My goodness, my darling, I love you.

- **Emma Jarman**

The Still Point

1982
Northwest mountains of North Carolina
Tracy is 27, Thomas is 12

It's been twelve years since I gave my baby away. Twelve years and five months since I was exiled to the Florence Crittenton Home for Unwed Mothers, where upper class white girls were sent to hide their pregnancies from the world. In 1970 we were expected to relinquish our baby at birth and never speak of it again.

~ ~ ~

The elderly Chestnut, lone survivor of the blight, stood as a centerpiece of all that could be surveyed from the expansive front porch. Others of its kind had once covered these Blue Ridge mountains like a shawl over shoulders on a cool evening. The deeply furrowed bark belied the ease with which an exotic fungus had slipped into the cambian and felled its brothers and sisters, once giants of these forests.

A singular sentinel – isolated, yet resilient. When weather was favorable, I would take my morning meditation in the rocking chair on the porch, facing the Chestnut. In spring the flowing white catkins waved like streamers on little girls' bike handles. Come summer the lush, saw-toothed, dark green leaves shaded the cultivated wildflowers beneath. Autumn equaled yellow blaze. But in late fall, when the burrs should have encased three chestnuts each, there were no harvests. The lone tree was sterile. Even so, it grew its canopy year by year, waiting patiently for a favorable wind to carry news of another survivor.

Most weeks I spent my day off from our business tending to the ample vegetable garden, which lay between the Chestnut and our log cabin. The ancient mountains, worn down now to lush rolling hills, grew a dark sandy loam that needed no amendments other than the occasional side dressing of composted manure. I worked in the partial shade of a four-foot diameter, ground-mounted satellite dish that provided live feeds of sports and the BBC. In early fall, with afternoon's slanted light, the bountiful harvest brought the last of the corn, the first of the autumn squashes, more tomatoes than I could put up, and the final raspberry yield.

I loved these mountains. It was here that I learned how to hoe the soil on top of the new potatoes; how to differentiate between the fringed gentian and the purple fringed orchid; how to be at the ready with one hundred pounds of black-oil sunflower seed when the migratory flocks of Evening Grosbeaks arrived in the front fields every April. I returned the hoe and the cultivator to the shed my husband had built, next to the chicken house he'd built as well. I poured grain into the self-feeder and retrieved eggs from the six straw-appointed nest boxes, apologizing to the unhappy brooding hen who pecked at my hand as I pulled her

92

warm egg from underneath. Normally the hens laid their eggs, then abandoned them to the morning pursuit of food. But two or three times a year each hen yielded to her instinctive need to raise a brood. If we wanted to manage the flock's size, we had to faithfully remove their egg each morning.

She didn't want to give it up, but I took it from her anyway. Heartbreaking.

~ ~ ~

I remembered that boy at the bank the previous morning, about the right age–twelve, brown eyes and light brown hair. His face looked familiar. I could find him again; ask about his birthday. Then I stopped, today's eggs in my basket, shook my head, and willed myself not to go down that unsettled path I had traveled so many times before.

Three years before, I'd followed a blonde-haired, brown-eyed boy at the spring Ramp Festival in Independence, Virginia. I pretended I was interested in the children's games, but his mother sensed my focus, glared.

Once, in Durham, I thought he sat next to his parents and an older girl at my favorite restaurant, Somethyme.

And he had called to me in the Duke Forest.

I had left my brown-eyed boy in Norfolk, Virginia. He could be anywhere, but almost certainly not in the little mountain town of West Jefferson, North Carolina.

~ ~ ~

As I approached the house, I saw the cardboard box on the front porch: A case of empty mason jars, pint and quart sizes. I couldn't be sure who had left them there, but I guessed it was Hollis Wild, the friend with the perfect name for mountain living. A practical gift, as I had so much bounty to put up for later, when it was needed. Now I would have to fill the jars: sweet pickles, tomato juice, green beans, black raspberry jam. . . all worthwhile, but so labor intensive. Harvesting, cleaning, cooking, canning absorbed all of my free time.

It had been four years since I'd followed my brilliant forest ecology professor to these lush hills, my Master's course load complete but my thesis still to write. In spite of the lure of the mountains and the man, I continued to long for something else. There was a restlessness in me that I attributed then to needing more culture, the stimulation of the academic environment, people my age, trips off the mountain. But I stayed put, feeling a discontent even as I became a part of the natural world I was surrounded by, gathering its sustenance: the satisfying feel of rich loam under my fingernails and the musky smell of the wood burning fireplace on a frosty night. And the creek walks with the dogs, when I filled my pack with dangling clusters of mulberries that tilted over the water, my river shoes keeping me safely balanced on the slippery stones.

The dogs. We were a "blended family" of husband Jim's two dogs from a previous marriage – Sadie the Beagle, and Joshua the Brittany Spaniel – together with Shantih, my Shepherd/Husky mix. Over our eight years in the cabin, we grew our pack by three more – Creature, Groundhog, and Lion. In those days we used the phrase "took in a stray" instead of "rescued." On any given night two or three dogs joined us on our bed to regulate our limbic systems – or put another way, to provide warmth and unconditional love. Looking back on a lifetime of bonding with dogs, I wonder if taking care of other emotional mammals was a way to practice my maternal instincts in the absence of my child.

I tried to get pregnant, but I didn't.

In spite of the dogs and the cabin and our authentic life, I still missed Durham. After six years, three times as long as any previous residence, my college town felt like the only home I had ever known. The life I had made at Duke and Durham had been my choice–the first time I had crafted an existence to suit my needs. No wonder I missed it.

And yet I had left boyfriend Doug for Jim, for a new adventure of homesteading and an outdoor outfitting business.

My unsettled path. I realize now that no matter how genuinely I wanted a more cultured life, what was really at issue is that I was never the one choosing the path. This was the deeper truth. I was always a rider on someone else's journey: first my parents, then birthfather Tommy, then Doug, now this professor. And I had followed Jim out of a place I wanted to stay.

Even though I followed these people, primarily men, I also eventually moved on from them–even Tommy. I was used to leaving, to closing the door and not looking back on all my work to create a life for myself wherever I ended up. Moving on was built into me from the time I was born. This was another truth.

The only time I embraced a move was in 1971, a year after my son's birth. My navy father, Capt. James O. Mayo, was ordered back to the D.C. area. Grateful to escape the compulsion to search for my baby in every passing stroller, I could focus on recreating my life. I could barely imagine how my Florence Crittenton friends, not from military families, lived with the very real possibility that their child might grow up in the next town, or the next block. An unthinkable torment.

And yet looking back, I can see that I never stopped searching for my baby in every passing stroller. Unlike the Chestnut, I wasn't sterile: I was a childless mother. A mother to my core, my sense of self rooted in the soil of growing and giving birth to a child I'd been forced to relinquish. Everything I was doing with my life in the mountains of North Carolina–gathering up my resources both externally and internally–was preparation for a journey that some part of me knew I had to take–my own life's path, which led to my son. He was the only one I had never moved on from. The bond between us held.

~~~

That fateful move to Portsmouth, Virginia in 1968. Of all of them, the one destined to change my life forever.

94

The hair-tinged-green-with-chlorine lifeguard. Cartwheels and broad jumps in the park on a sultry summer night. Giggling explorations in the navy chapel. The sweatshirt around my shoulders on a surprisingly cool evening. The hard buttons on the bare blue and white striped mattress pressing into my hip as I accepted the full weight of him. The realization, the fear, the earnest need for my mother. And the pink and yellow pills on my nightstand.

I can hear my mother's voice:

"This is what you get for playing with fire. Just what did you THINK was going to happen?" Mom handing me two girdles and proclaiming: "Wear these every day to school. Make sure you only change into your gym clothes in the bathroom stall."

In my brown-and-yellow-striped footie pajamas, the eavesdropping at the top of the stairs.

Mom's voice again: "We could send her to Seattle, make up some story about my parents."

And Dad's reply: "We could say she went to Seattle, but we could send her to a home for unwed mothers instead."

And so it was done.

What might have happened if my mother, as a mother, had acknowledged the exorbitant price I would pay, and stood up for me? If I had been free to help with the baby when I could, while back in school, eventually to college? If Tommy and I had gotten married and reclaimed our young son? All the TM and LSD that I turned to in crisis, the ways I tried to find a unity of being, a still point of connection in the world: It was all about discovering and holding on to the connection to my son.

~ ~ ~

The canning days passed. I put up my lime pickles, the spicy tomato juice, my serrano-infused corn, the mulberry jelly–and beets, green beans, okra. One day we drove down the mountain to the city below to visit museums and a truck farm, and returned with a new hen and rooster, the heirloom breed known as Plymouth Rock. We would breed and allow the hen to raise a few chicks, contribute to the genetic diversity, before the rooster would grow bold enough to challenge the resident Rhode Island Red–and therefore, be fated to chicken and dumplings.

I watched the Chestnut drop its leaves, pulling its energy down to last another winter. This deeply rooted survivor, the landmark of my life.

On a chilly fall night when Jim taught at Appalachian State University as an adjunct, I stoked the fire, retrieved the precious photograph of my infant son, now twelve years old. Tucked into the same scalloped blue envelope from 1970, a still ocean hidden in a box of note cards, left bottom drawer, my nightstand, the same home it had occupied through all my moves. I examined his tiny face and imagined how he might look today.

I placed the photo on my folded knees, closed my eyes and started my mantra. I would practice my TM, I would touch the peace and calm of absolute Being, and wherever I went the universe would keep us connected, through a silvery thread, with me at one endpoint and my son at the other.

- **Tracy Mayo**

After the Ice Storm

Old friend now there is no one alive
*who remembers when you were young**
wrote Merwin to a walnut tree, and when I saw
the oak tree dying–the sleeping giant whose shade
I had rested under with my newborn daughter,
whose branches sprawled across the yard,
my shelter and comfort–I thought about my mother,
born on the icy plains. When the storms came
did she, too, wash the dishes by a lantern's light?
Lose something she held dear?
There is no one left to ask these questions now.

The icing started before dawn. The trees,
already weakened by drought, bent under
a thick coating. The first to fall
took out the power lines. I heard the clicks
of flickering lights, and before I had the words
to name it my body knew the loss. I dug deeper
under covers, gathering my heat.

If it had been gradual. If it had been our time.
I could have curled my daughter's
fingers around the evergreen leaves.
Spread my mother's quilt under the canopy,
thumbing the stitching of her name.
I could have climbed the knotty trunk
and felt my girlhood return to me,
at peace in filtered blue air.

That evening, I lay in the darkened house
listening. All night, I heard the old trees splitting,
a city steeped in crashing umber. When it was my oak's
turn, it came down softly, a sway of branches
that could no longer bear their weight.

In the morning I woke to the music of chainsaws.
In the rearranged landscape, the birds
still found a perch in cluttered limbs.

The downed oak–still green, still leafy–
lay two stories long, bedded into the crushed
hay-colored grass. I carried my daughter
out to say goodbye, knowing all too well
she won't remember this, that she may only
ever know the wound, and not what was lost.

- Sara Rosenberg

*from W. S. Merwin's poem Elegy for a Walnut Tree

Ghosts

I thought the ghosts would come later,
but, already, here they are,
my ancestor, between you and
me.

For years, when I walked in the woods, when the dust tracked up my legs,
when the exhalationsof plants and their flowers
endriled through my body, the ghosts of animals
shadowed me.

Some I could identify as species: a mule deer or black bear or ruffed grouse, but
then the ghosts came who were just the presence
of the lives here before our divisions and your lighting
of flames.

The ghosts who followed me made no sound and had no eyes or faces, and yet
they took me in.
The lack in their voices was like an extinction or the passing of
a meteor.

The ghosts delivered no message and I pricked my ears for none.
Of course, I was startled, but I sought no reason.
I came to expect the ghosts, even to long for them.
I stopped my habit of carrying flint and steel.

I became agreeable to most invitations that stayed below the treeline.
The animals came to me like a mist even as the glaciers above us
dwindled to granite sepulchers, and I passed through the hot woods feeling my
breath as a habitat for what were not things.

- Matt Daly

The Letters

To my friend Annie, I want to tell you something. I had a dream about you one night, we were together, we were holding each other, I couldn't kiss you.
I held my self out and looked at your face.
I wish I could kiss you but I stay back, not really holding back.
I have love.

It was less than a three-mile bike ride from my house on Springtown Road into town, across land that had been flattened thousands of years earlier by the meandering Walkill River. When I got to the pharmacy parking lot, Larry was waiting. He told me he wanted to take me to his favorite spot. So I followed him down a quiet oak-lined side street, slipping through the golf club at the end of Huguenot and out the other side. Our bikes bounced over the railroad ties until we came to a turnoff, a grassy path that led to the river.

I didn't get to spend much time with Larry in school. He wasn't in my homeroom, so our classes didn't line up. Sixth-graders had math and science in the room on one side of the hall; for language arts and science we swapped to the other side. Depending on what period gym fell, Larry and I would sometimes pass each other coming or going. But we had lunch together, and if we ate fast enough and the weather wasn't too bad, we had half an hour for outdoor recess. I had a couple of girlfriends in my school, but most of the time I hung out with Larry. Second half of the year, in place of gym they combined the two classes, and Larry and I ended up in art to-gether.

The art teacher was an impossibly skinny, dark-haired, tall man named Mr. Engersoll. To this day I hold him in my mind next to the way I imagine Abraham Lincoln. Mr. Engersoll was soft-spoken and kind, and best of all he let us do pretty much whatever we wanted. Every class he would give lessons on various techniques with clay, paints, calligraphy, origami, pen and ink, wood blocks, screen-printing, and then he allowed us freedom.

It was in that room I learned everything I would ever need to know about Larry. That although he felt he didn't fit into school—and in many ways he didn't—he belonged here, sur-rounded by art supplies, tools, paper; any medium he touched he became quickly skilled at. That was when he started sending me the letters.

The letters always came in standard, white envelopes, but that was the only thing ordinary about them. At first, he simply added a flourish or two to my name and my address; the numbers became dancing twists and swirls, letters bloomed into flowers or trees. Sometimes he would extend them to touch the top of the envelope. He would darken and thicken some letters and leave the others skinny and plain. He would make each word and each number a different size so they bounced up and down on the paper. He started drawing pictures around my name, even surrounding the 10-cent stamp—shooting stars, peering eyes, arrows, flowers, birds, a sail-boat on the horizon where a smiling sun was just beginning to rise. Once, just in order to make the address legible, someone at the post office had handwritten: New Paltz, NY 12561. I think that one was my favorite, his unconscious way of using art to defy society and its rules.

Of course, I could see that Larry's address—also elaborately decorated—was a PO Box in Esopus, a hamlet outside town, but it wasn't until I started driving, years later, that I realized every time Larry met me at the pharmacy parking lot, he was adding twenty-four round-trip miles on his bike, and that his return home was mostly uphill.

The letters I received in the mail were often pages long, front and back, others only a paragraph or two—always with a detailed drawing tucked inside. Sometimes he wrote me letters only hours after spending the day in school together, passing notes back and forth. On those scraps of paper there wasn't a break or punctuation where Larry's words ended and mine followed. Our handwriting was nearly indistinguishable. Our spelling equally atrocious.

The following year, we were allowed to pick mini-courses.

Annie,

The reason I didn't hand my mini-course thing in is because I don't know what you're doing 3 and seventh period on tue. And thur. So what are you doing. You have to tell me I got in trouble just for dear, sweet you. Now doesn't that make you feel good?

Ha ha

In the letters he wrote from home he usually began by telling me what music he was listening to: Bob Dylan, Allman Brothers, Joni Mitchell, The Rolling Stones. Larry loved Mick Jagger. He loved the song "Angie," when it was number one on the charts—October 1973. I cannot hear that song—one of the most plaintive and heartbreaking love songs ever written—without thinking of Larry, and remembering that overcast day on the middle school playground when he taught me the melody and lyrics.

By seventh grade we were a couple. Matched up like the other kids in our grade. Michael and Terry. Jean and Todd. Gordie and Melanie.

Annie,

Now I am listening to Blue Sky, Eat a Peach. Rather appropriate. I'm going to tell you how your letter affected me. I don't know if it has happened to you but I while I was reading it, all my blood, well not all of it, ran to my head, strange? And, you don't ever have to say sorry to me. We're equal, and when you say your sorry your lowering yourself. I don't want you to b doing that. Blue Sky's are so beautiful but not as beautiful as you are. I'm lost without you, like today. I love you. There is no one on this big earth like you and there never will be. What freaks me out is what did I ever do, or what am I that can be right for you. I don't know but I sure am glad. I love you.

The whole school knew Larry and I were made for each other. I was the writer; he was the artist. I wanted us to last forever, but of course, we couldn't.

~~~

I barely knew my dad when my brother, Paul, and I were returned to him. After our parents got divorced, we lived with our mom and her boyfriend on a commune outside of Woodstock, visiting our dad in New Paltz only sporadically. When Mom found another new boyfriend, she followed him out to California and dropped us back off with Dad. She only superficially fought for custody of us, that was pretty obvious, but to be honest neither my brother nor I wanted to move in with her new boyfriend. The last one had been bad enough. The summer before I started school, before I met Larry, was the loneliest time of my life.

~~~

Eighth grade, those boyfriend and girlfriend couplings began to get serious. They didn't last very long, maybe a few weeks or so before they broke up, and then, without skipping a beat, swapped with one another to form another pair. You could get detention for kissing in the hallway between classes, but doing it was a way to signal ownership—no matter how temporary. It was a demonstration of true love, but perhaps more importantly, it was the blueprint for the nascent sexuality that was just around the corner. What we did now, while we were still in middle school, would be the identity that would follow us all through high school. Who would be the good girl? The cockteaser? The wild boy every girl wanted? The loose girl—sometimes referred to as a skank? Which couple would stay together for the next four years, dramatically breaking up, only to fall tearfully into each other's arm once again? And the ever-important, Who would be the most popular?

Larry was my boyfriend and that year, Margot was my best friend. It was apparent—at least to me—that Margot's mother had an odd investment in her daughter's approval rating, and would do anything from buying her a Volkswagon Beetle convertible, yellow with a white top, to giving her permission to have the very first boy-girl party in her finished basement. The finished basement being Mecca of the Make-out Party.

"We need to write it all down and it has to be even pairs." Margot sat at the end of her bed, atop her perfectly made pink-ruffled bedspread. She held a pad of paper on her knees, and a pencil in her hand.

"Well, duh," I said.

"M&M, for sure," Margot began. "Right?"

Other than Larry and I, Michael and Michelle had been going out the longest, long enough to have earned a nickname. When I nodded, she wrote down their names. We had been given a cap of ten people, five couples. We needed to come up with two more couples before any of them broke up or someone decided to have another party on the same day. Like most things in life, timing was crucial.

"Okay, who else?'

We came up with Todd and Melanie; then Gordie and Brenda, the new girl who had just moved from New York City. Margot numbered the couples one through five. At the bottom she added Annie and Larry, Margot and Russ.

We were relieved no one declined the invitation, which would have upset the configuration, and even more relieved that Saturday night, everyone showed up. It's not like everyone who came didn't know exactly what was going on, but we were all terrified. At first, the girls stayed pretty close together, while the boys congregated around the food table that Margot and I had set up: cold liters of Coke and Sprite, bowls of potato chips and Fritos, and dip made of Lipton's onion mix and sour cream. We had folded paper napkins into triangles and made two neat stacks of plastic cups. As promised, Margot's mother stayed upstairs.

As our party was beginning to flop, someone dimmed the overhead lights, and slightly increased the volume on the tape deck. Like a game of musical chairs, couples awkwardly tried to choose the best spot. M&M took the couch. Melanie and Todd were on the floor against the far wall. Gordie and Brenda slipped out into the hall. Michael and Michelle hid behind the bar. Larry and I ended up on one of the wide club chairs. We held hands for a while, we whispered, we talked about how we felt about each other. But nothing else.

Annie—I'm really sorry that I made you feel downgraded. Well you see, the other day, Saturday at night I felt really strange and I still do. Sometimes I feel like an experiment that some doctor put me under this circumstance (my life) and I wonder. Because I feel like this might be be-cause I'm strange but I'm not strange I just don't know myself. Blah…blah..blah.

When I read through the pages of my diary now, I hear a thirteen-year-old girl lamenting that she was unattractive. That something was wrong with her. That Larry didn't love her. He loved someone else. I described the fun we had. The bikes rides. Sneaking into Minnnewaska to swim at Split Rock. Bowling. Getting high. I recorded the fights we had. How sorry I was after we made up. How sorry he was. I wrote that I blamed myself, but when I look back, I see my words as insincere. I knew the reason Larry and I weren't making out, holding hands, or rubbing our groins together, pressed up against the lockers; it was something different altogether. I didn't know what, but I knew it wasn't me.

Love,

I'm in bed. Wish you were here. Why is it I love you and we can't be alone? It doesn't make sense. You're so beutiful, so beutiful. You won't ever believe how I feel when you smile. Beutiful.

What you dream is beutiful. In vain? No not quite. I dream of that always. Ignorant? Just as ignorant as I am. What leads me to say I'm not experienced at all. Not with someone I love your the only one I love, only one I ever love and the only one I ever will love. I'm so sure. We are perfect. You agree? We are refugees from the normal life. We're on the same level. I lack physical contact with you. Kiss me, in school

I'll kiss you. I love you.

~ ~ ~

Larry and I didn't stop being best friends, but in high school I became more involved with my girlfriends, the school newspaper, the track team, and boys. And Larry discovered the theater. He auditioned and got a part in the senior show, "Three Penny Opera," the only freshman cast. He was magnificent. The goofy, awkward, taller-than-average, muscular ninth-grade boy became someone very different when he was onstage. He became a swan. It was as if he had been born knowing how to sculpt, paint, draw, carve wood blocks, how to sing with a strong passionate voice, and how to act. In makeup and costume, Larry had that presence only true performers have. The charisma you can't see on film, but vibrates in your bones when you see it live.

MY BEAUTIFUL ANNIE,

YOU HAVE NO IDEA THE HEAD YOU GET WHEN THIRTY PEOPLE SUDDENLY ACCOMPANY YOU IN A SONG THAT IS YOUR SONG. IT'S THE MOST FANTASTIC FEELING AND THEN YOU HAVE TO BE LOUDER AND I ALSO GET RID OF COOPED UP ANXIETY.

And Larry knew how to dance. He began taking lessons. There were only two schools of dance in New Paltz. There was Susan Slotnick, who taught tap, modern, and improv in a studio above a crafts store, and there was Fred DeMayo, who taught The Balanchine Method of ballet. Larry wasn't the only boy in our school who took ballet, so I don't think anyone thought much of it. I certainly didn't. I was in awe of him.

High school was also when he and I began sneaking into the auditorium during lunch period. The cafeteria—most of school—was unbearable to us both. The double doors to the theater were never locked and no one was ever in there. It was mostly dark, except for the lights that ran along the rows of seats. The velvet curtains were pulled open. There was no set, unless there was a production underway, so ladders and ropes, props stacked against the back wall, brooms, boxes, the sound equipment were all visible, the entire landscape of the theater behind us while Larry and I would sing songs from Broadway musicals, "A Chorus Line," "Cabaret," and "A Little Night Music." We would perform in any empty house, to and only, for each other.

There was no moment when Larry and I decided not to be romantic partners, but at some point, it was just assumed I would become interested in other boys for other reasons; but that didn't change our attachment to each other, or slow down the letter writing. Love has reason that reason knows not of.

And that reason is jealousy.

Annie
I think I'll get right down to what I said before- anyway yesterday I got mad at Greg Peterson. He gave you the eyes. I was going to do something but it was the end of the day so I didn't.

I was jealous but wouldn't be to look at you, you BEAUTIFUL FELUPSC-VOS hunk of a woman. Ha ha "Don't let it go to your head" Anyway I love you. And doon't forget it you bone-head. I' not going camping I hope. I'd go to your house.

I started making out with boys. That is certainly not the right term, but there isn't another word to describe it. There should be. The kissing occurred sometimes at the drive-in. Maybe outside in the woods. In someone's skunky-smelling, smoke-filled bedroom. Or on the flatbed of a pick-up in the middle of a corn field. It was 1975, and the Women's Movement was ignited, but somehow the proclamations of empowerment, taking ownership of one's own body, and the message that a girl did not need to identify herself by the approval she could garner from a boy, had not trickled down to me. Even if it had, it was too late. I was never wooed, never dated, per se. I made-out with beer-breathed boys who had no interest in who I was, nor to be honest, did I have any interest in them. I wasn't aware that should have been a prerequisite on both sides. So instead, I was badly and forcefully French-kissed, and humiliatingly finger-fucked.

Still, in the midst of all that, I wanted Larry all to myself.

Annie
Yes, I mean no, you're not stupid to be mad at me when I talk to other girls. If you weren't I wouldn't love you like I do. Or what I mean is as much as I do. I love everything about you but, oh forget it. Anyway when you get mad I know you care. Right. But it doesn't give you the flying neurosis does it? I don't really have time to write to my favorite movie star but I will feel guilty if I don't.

When we started eleventh grade I was tired of my wrestling team crush cuming on my stomach, in my parents' bed when they were out of town. I wanted a boyfriend, a real one, even if that meant hiding behind a half-truth and officially breaking up with Larry. Such was the make-believe very real drama of high school. It didn't change anything between us, not really, but what it did mean was that I was free to explore my sexuality on my own terms.

That year, I went to the prom with Jeff DeBois, and Larry went with

Julia Summers. I was livid. By that point, I understood that Larry did not like girls, not in that way, and more than ever I wanted him to belong to me. Julia was overweight, a year older, and a theater person. I knew it was all fake, but I hated it. Hated her.

The Stonewall riots were long past, but "Will and Grace" was fifteen years away. Ellen wouldn't come out for another twenty. And while I wasn't entirely sure what it meant I knew Larry was gay.

Still, I kept this realization to myself—and in ways, from myself—aware that what I knew would be dangerous to Larry. There would never be any discussion about it between us, no moment of reveal. The truth simply presented itself. It made the love we had for each other greater.

We both wanted out of high school so badly. I had taken extra classes all year, passed my Regents exams midyear, and graduated early. Twenty-five dollars got you an application to four different state universities. I was accepted by all four, but I chose the one known for its professional programs in music, dance, theater, and writing: SUNY Purchase. The plan was that Larry would come with me, and we would have four years together, to reinvent ourselves—he to dance and me to write, finally to be free. Then Larry got accepted into the Joffrey School of Ballet, and I went to school without him. I went to Westchester; he went to the City.

1:20 April 19, 1979

Dear Annie,

I'm in central park, it's so gorgeous- azalea, cherry, daffodils, all in blossom, grass is green, sun is shining, LOVELY, wish you were here.

I got a scholarship with American Ballet Center, (Joffrey School!) for the summer season, wow..!

(got it yesterday)
Love ya,
bye bye
your broda
Larry
(twiddle toes)

~~~

SUNY Purchase was where I was meant to be. Jugglers on the quad, frisbee on the lawn, musicians on the brick wall. Even back then, gays, lesbians, drag queens, bisexuals, blended into the student body as moody writers, anxious dancers, snobby actors, and visual arts majors covered in paint or smelling of clay. So much so that pretty much everyone—at least a large percentage of the women—experimented with being with other women or other men. It was kind of the thing to do. I was never very good at it, but I tried.

106

My roommate and I decided on a time and place, a night our other roommate would be gone for the weekend. We both got into bed, both in our bra and panties. We even lit candles. We kissed once or twice and gave up. But it was enough to call myself bisexual and casually let Larry know about the new me. Maybe I wanted to be Purchase-cool. Or just add to my abstract list of sexual exploits. But mostly, it was my way of connecting with Larry. Joining the club. Seeking his approval by showing him mine.

Living in New York City, Larry became openly and vibrantly gay. During the day, he trained to be a dancer, weekends and evenings he wore black pants, a white dress shirt and served appetizers. Whenever I was in the city I would visit, taking the subway from Grand Central to Union Square. The Joffrey School was in SoHo. I climbed the steep narrow stairs to the dance studio.

"You look incredible," I said. I walked past the dancers splayed out in the hall—wrapping the long ribbons of their pointe shoes, bandaging their toes, entirely indifferent to a civilian like me—stepping tentatively over their long legs.

"So do you," he said. He had grown into an entirely different person than he had been in high school. The ugly duckling? Pinocchio turned into a boy? A man? As if he were finally where he belonged. I so badly had wanted him to have come to school with me, but he had skipped that step and was already in the professional world.

I probably could never have convinced him to come to school with me instead, but often wish, if only I had.

"Come inside." Larry took my hand and led me into the studio. It was mostly empty but for a few women and one man standing together at the barre seemingly deep in conversation, at the same time bending, stretching, arms overhead. Dancers never stop moving.

"This is where you dance?"

"It is," Larry told me.

He was happy, so I was happy.

"I'm not in the company yet, you know. But who knows?"

"You will be."

I could see Larry standing next to me, and I could see him in the wall of mirrors, a familiar, and yet faraway image from my memory. His voice was the same, as were his dark eyes, olive skin and full lips. Larry might have been Hispanic, or part black, of Mediterranean heritage or Native American. He was shirtless and sweaty, his ribs and stomach rippled with muscles, his posture was perfect. He was taller in all ways. He wore shorts and black ballet slippers. His toes slightly turned out, but what once looked awkward was now graceful and strong.

He was beautiful.

"C'mon."

Larry grabbed his bag from the hall, pulled a T-shirt over his head, changed into his sneakers, and he took me to see his apartment. It was a small studio in a nice building. The sun, as it began to set, bathed the room in yellow light.

"It's so you," I said. I felt so young at that moment. Far from having my own place, a place I paid for, and furnished. Larry had done it. He had gotten out, and he had a beautiful life.

~ ~ ~

The spring before I graduated from Purchase, I visited Larry again. By this time, I was hearing about one boyfriend, and then another. He got a cat. More artwork decorated his apartment, and a mobile made of bamboo poles strung together at all different angles.

"I have the key to Robert's apartment," Larry said.

"Is that your boyfriend?"

Larry smiled. "No," he said. "Robert Joffrey. He's away and wants me to water his plants."

My first thought was that Larry must have made such an impression with the ballet school that soon he'd be accepted in the company. He'd made it. But another part of me worried. I knew the older-man-younger-boy relationship was common in the gay community, but Larry was so kind and generous and loving, vulnerable and naive. Something felt wrong about this. It was just a sense I had, the way I had known Larry was gay when we were in eighth grade, except this feeling did not feel good.

"Do you want to see it?" Larry asked. "It's incredible. It's huge. Wait until you see what you can see out the windows. The whole park."

There was a lot of coke floating around New York City in those days. No one thought twice about it. Larry and I were blitzed when we got on the train across town. We walked from 72nd to Robert Joffrey's apartment. The way the doorman nodded to him; the way Larry knew more about the apartment than someone just coming to water the plants. I wasn't a prude, but I didn't want anyone taking advantage of my best friend. It made me angry, but I didn't say a thing.

By the time we ran out of coke, poked through the fridge, smoked pot, and watched TV, it was late.

"We should just stay here," Larry said.

It was like that then, people were looser, less protective, fewer material boundaries. Crashing on someone's couch. Borrowing their car. Staying over in someone's apartment without their permission. Or maybe I was just so much younger then; those years when I didn't think very much about consequences. I barely considered what was right or wrong.

Be free, do whatever you want as long as it doesn't hurt anyone.

Remember that?

The four bedrooms—each in a different color theme, black, pink, yellow, and baby blue, each with a king-sized bed and too many pillows—were out of the question. We grabbed extra blankets and pillows from the linen closet and laid them out on the floor. With the expanse of Central Park before us, lit up by street lamps, and car headlights reflected on the ceiling as they drove down Central Park West, we lay side-by-side, talking in the darkness. He told me stories about New York, things he had seen on the subway, gossip at the dance studio. I told him about Purchase, the boy who had such a crush on me he put his fist through a wall when I turned him down. We talked about New Paltz, what we had heard about the kids we went to school with. The coke was wearing off, the pot was making me sleepy. The long pauses were getting longer. I thought we would both be asleep in a few minutes.

Larry turned his head toward me. "Will you have sex with me?"

"What?"

"We love each other. We never did it. Will you do it now? With me?"

My best friend, so gay, so beautiful and successful in the world he had found? It was confusing, and it took me awhile before I could decide whether he was serious or not, before I could decide how to answer.

"Larry, I can't do that."

"Why?" His voice, and the expression on this face, told me he was more than just hurt.

"Don't be mad at me," I said. "Of course, I love you."

"Why then?" he asked. "Why not? You're not attracted to me?"

It wasn't like me to refuse, especially when I was high. Fuck, I had been with guys I didn't even like. I suppose I wasn't attracted to him, not that way. Not in the way I needed boys to treat me in those days—badly. The way I needed them to want me—badly. But I had to say something, offer some explanation.

"I'm a girl," I said. "I can get pregnant. You can't understand that. You don't get it."

"What don't I get?" He was angry, I knew, but not at me.

Not really.

I think back now and wonder if all Larry wanted was to find a way out. If there had been one, would he have taken it? Larry's life was so much harder than I ever understood. It wasn't 2022. It was 1982. New York was scary. It was gritty and crime-ridden. Graffiti reigned. As did the crack epidemic. Times Square was a cesspool of porn shops and peep shows. Every morning you could find a used needle or two on the street beside the curb. Harvey Milk had been assassinated three years before in San Francisco. Only two short years ago, homosexuality was a crime in New York State; in most other states, it still was. Larry was broken by my firmness. He was as surprised and hurt by my answer as I was by his anger.

It would be only a few more years, when the AIDS crisis was terrorizing and terrifying, I came to realize that—in all likelihood—the fortuity of my decision that night may have saved my life.

I didn't see much of Larry after the night we slept at Joffrey's, and by 1988, when Robert Joffrey died, I was married and had a one-year-old son, Sam. Larry and I talked often on the phone. I listened to stories about his life, his successes, his latest works of art, his boyfriends, but I didn't get into the city much, if at all. I hadn't seen him in person for years. A part of me was embarrassed to tell him about my conventional life, my husband, my house in the suburbs. I didn't want Larry to see me differently than he always had. Yet, I knew he still believed in me, never doubted I would be published one day, believed in me just as much as he had in middle school, and high school, college, and even now.

Then, Larry was diagnosed with HIV.

July 27, 1990

Hi Annie,

It was great talking to you. I guess I knew what I was doing in second grade when I noticed you were more than special.

Here is photographs of my King + Queen watercolors. The colors are more vibrant and at the same time earthy and natural—this photo allows you to see.

Please, I wold like to read the short story you wrote recently. Either when I visit or if it's possible to be sent to me.

Anyway. I can't wait to see you and your family.

Love 4ever

Lar

I never considered that I wouldn't want to see him, but I wasn't sure if I should touch him. Hug him? Or what to do when he drank from one of our water glasses. This was a plague, and there was a lot of speculation, rumor, and fear about how AIDs was transmitted. Pretty much the only thing people agreed upon was that it was a death sentence.

~~~

Not by design, at least not consciously, it was a weekday and my husband was at work. I picked Larry up at the Westport train station, with Sam sleeping in his carseat in the back, his head flopped to the side, as if he was a stuffed toy. We drove to my house, my yellow house with red shutters, the front door painted colonial green, and an actual white picket fence.

Our time together went quickly—both comfortable and awkward, hopeful and desperate —and it was time to leave so Larry could catch the train back to the city. I left the dishes unwashed in the sink. I would decide how to handle that later.

There was nothing to stop the late-afternoon sun from turning the train platform to white heat. Sam had fallen asleep in his baby carrier, heavy on my shoulders. Sweat was pooling underneath it and running down my back. If Sam could remember that day, when he was year and a half and Mommy's high school friend came to visit, I'm sure he'd remember that he liked Larry, that Larry was special.

I didn't want to say goodbye, but I wanted to get home. Everything felt topsy-turvy, as if I were straddling two worlds—who I was and who I had become, and neither felt particularly real—but I wasn't present, there on the platform with Larry, waiting for the 3:55 Metro North to Grand Central Terminal. Where had my life gone? I hadn't made much of it, other than getting married, having a kid, and writing mediocre short stories that were collecting rejections. Who was I kidding?

Before we could hear it, the single headlight of the train was visible far down the tracks. The pitch of the whistle got higher as it sped toward us. When the doors slid open, Larry turned to hug me goodbye. He tipped his head to one side. I moved to the other and our faces met. In that moment I had the choice to turn away or let our lips touch. We kissed. Our first and last.

~ ~ ~

A year and half passed. Larry was no longer dancing. He was sick. He was no longer working. He was supported by the government on disability. I will always remember exactly where I was standing when we last spoke, in my kitchen, leaning on the door to the basement, twisting the phone cord.

"You're going on vacation?" I said into the phone. "To Puerto Rico?"

I was incredulous. He was excited.

Since getting married, I had traveled a lot. My husband went to conferences that we often turned into family trips. But Larry had never been on a plane before. Never left the country. I don't think he had gone much farther than upstate New York.

"Yeah, we have tickets. Me and Roberto."

Larry and I never talked about AIDs. I would ask him how he was feeling, but that was the extent of it. I wouldn't let myself think about what a horrible friend I was being. I wasn't aware of how terrified I was of losing him. How angry I was at him.

"You're going on vacation on welfare?" I said. "I mean, is that what you're supposed to be spending that money on?"

To this day, as deeply as I will forever regret my words, I am impressed how quickly and acutely on target Larry shot back. He had never criticized me before. His love for me was immutable. Now, I had broken that trust.

"Well, what do you do to deserve what you have? Your house? All the trips you take. You're a housewife," he said. "Your husband takes care of you. What's the difference between you and me?"

After that, my memory of the conversation gets blurry, but eventually, somehow we got off the phone. Larry didn't call me back to make up, and I didn't call him, although I knew I was the one who should be apologizing. I was too ashamed, but not about the phone call. We had certainly had arguments before.

No, because I picked a fight to protect myself. I could close my eyes and not have to see the weight he would lose. Not have to hear about the number of T-cells he wouldn't have in his beautiful body, or witness the Karposi sarcoma that would appear on his gentle face, his legs, his torso. I didn't have to share his fear, nor feel his pain.

How many months went by before I finally called to say: Hey, Larry. I'm so sorry. I was a jerk. It was stupid of me. I miss you. I love you. But I got no answer. Another week before I tried again. Another month? Then another. Before I dug out his parents' phone number in Esopus, September 1993, and his mother told me.

"Sweetheart," his mother said, not unkindly. "Larry died three weeks ago."

~ ~ ~

I saved all of Larry's letters from sixth grade to the very last one he wrote to me in 1990, wrapped in a piece of cloth and tied with a thin leather cord, as if I knew one day I would need them. After twenty-three years in an unhappy marriage, contemplating whether or not to leave my husband, I took them out. I lay them on my dining room table, only to find my table wasn't large enough to hold them all. I needed the entire floor to see them all at once. I sat crossed-legged for hours, slipping them out of their ornate envelopes, reading each one. I did not try to stop my sobbing. I needed to feel the sharp, cutting pain in my throat and my chest. I knew there would never be anyone who believed in me as he did, who loved me as ferociously.

- **Nora Raleigh**

Howth, Ireland

It has happened before,
this rift, this exclusion,
this avoidance of each other.

As if we had been ordered
to quarantine for unknown weeks
on opposite sides of a too small house.

We walk past a line of parked cars
and I think, which one would I choose,
which one would I drive away?

But to where? because there is
no distance far enough
to be close enough to stay.

The stone walls of Howth line the shore,
built to keep the sea from
pounding arguments with the town.

What if no one thought it through,
how mortar could erode,
let in wildness, let out relief

We watch distant waves flicker, while
our regrets pave tunnels, once long and dim,
now too short and too bright.

Still, our willful hands seek out and grasp
each other, our touch so warm it surprises,
despite the cold between us.

- Rachel Baum

Meeting

I'm in the passenger seat of our old Honda in the dirt lot next to the ramshackle Galveston strip mall that houses a bait shop, a laundromat, five vacant storefronts and an AA meeting. It's late afternoon and hot. My door's open. The driver's side is permanently closed by an accordion pleat I have no memory of acquiring. I've been parked for what feels like a long time but is probably only ten minutes.

My girlfriend Bonnie is inside. I'm waiting for her. Or for something to happen.

There's three inches left in the fifth of Jack Daniels under the seat. I'm saving it for emergencies. That, and seven blue take-the-edge-off pills, hidden from Bonnie.

Should I take one? Or wait?

I don't deserve Bonnie. She's unbelievably beautiful and sweet. And weak. She decided to attend meetings again after cutting her hair with the tiny scissors on her Swiss Army knife. She highlighted the remains with a pink Magic Marker this afternoon in our motel room, which has no TV or air conditioning. She says it's her Joan of Arc look, an artistic statement, perfect for her floundering singing career. Bonnie performs in bars. This poses problems, given our respective addictions. But soon after the haircut she'd asked me to drive her to a meeting. They hold several every day. The four o'clock is her favorite. It ends right before the cocktail hour, which she finds helpful. Not that we've ever had proper cocktails with stemmed glasses and olives.

My shirt smells wet and sour.

I wish the radio worked. My shitty hometown station plays country-western, but even that would be enough. My phone battery's dead. Again. A trickle of saline crawls down my spine toward the soggy waistband of my boxers.

I consider a walk but can't make up my mind to go. Besides, there's no place to walk to. Just heat-softened asphalt, red Texas dust and some sorry businesses unlikely to welcome me.

Meetings last an hour most days. I drive Bonnie because she lost her license. Not that having a license makes you a better driver. She stopped asking me to come inside with her around the time we got evicted from our apartment, just after the driller canned my ass because the derrickman ratted me out for "safety violations endangering the rig." That's when Bonnie started spending her tips on our pay-by-the-day motel and saying, "All use is abuse." She stopped mentioning marriage.

Marriage licenses don't make people better partners, either.

There's nothing to do but swelter and pick my cuticles. I could read, but what would I read? There was a box of books in the trunk. What happened to that box? The only literature in our motel room was from the Gideon Society. I kept meaning to replace my lost library card so that I'd have a book in the glovebox for these occasions, waiting for my girlfriend to twelve-step. But I hadn't bothered with a new card, it's just another sort of "license."

I'm a poor planner.

Soon I will be thirty years old. I never planned on that, either.

A crack runs across the windshield. I marvel at how straight it is, parallel to the dashboard. Was it there when I bought the car? No matter. The windshield is shit, like the car itself. But as I examine it, my salty chin resting on the split Naugahyde, someone limps from the end of the parking lot toward the strip mall door Bonnie entered. He wears brown corduroys, a long-sleeved shirt, and a vest. The vest seems odd, a layer of unnecessary clothing on a ninety-five-degree day.

Then I recognize him: Mr. Wellman, my high school English teacher. Same wire-rimmed glasses as twelve years ago. Same odd, foot-dragging gait. Hair below the collar. Enviable auburn mustache long enough to interfere with lunch. Still wearing his signature fringed leather vest, or an exact replica. The only cool guy on the faculty, which was mostly colorless, ageless women. His "progressive" bent caused occasional skirmishes with the school board. He'd guided my taste in books. He listened when I talked, a new experience for me. He'd hosted parties in his trailer. Being invited made me feel chosen, special.

I didn't know then, but I know now: I'm not special.

He urged me to consider college at University of Texas at Austin, where he'd gone, and offered a letter of recommendation. He thought I could get in. The town had a cool vibe, a lively music scene he thought I'd enjoy. I thought so too, then. Somehow, I'd abandoned the application, or in truth, procrastinated, squandering it in favor of big money promised by the oil fields.

His letter mentioned my "keen intellect" and "unusual analytic acumen." I wish I had a copy of it in my hands right now.

Maybe I could try again, apply now. But how would I explain where I'd been in the dozen years since high school, when I wasn't quite sure myself?

Mr. Wellman had introduced me to George Saunders, Denis Johnson, bell hooks.

And hashish.

My quadriceps twitch, encouraging me to rise and greet Mr. Wellman, whose first name I don't recall, or never knew. I stop myself, not because of AA's confidentiality rules, but because I can't think of what to say to him or to the people inside.

I could sit quietly in the back row.

Sweat creeps down my neck, but I'm suddenly cold. I feel some decision being reached, at a cellular level. A now-or-never choice to stand and follow him into the cinderblock building. I stop thinking and rise.

Everything turned out different than I thought it would.

- **Susan Hettinger**

115

All Of It

This talk across morning is coffee, and rage.
Until I taste your nipple. Bite your thigh.
Suspend myself above this explosive void,
And laugh-
Like a jester
Waiting on the executioner.

- Korey Wallace

Sales Pitch

Helen Carpenter's office was big enough. It took them four strides to come to her coffin-sized desk. A leather couch sat off to one side in a separate sitting area, but Brian had envisioned pitching their invention to a guy in an expensive suit walking to another meeting. He wanted to make a pitch as if he was on Shark Tank and not to a director of procurement. Helen, a petite woman in her forties was the antithesis of a mogul.

At the moment, Helen was not even in the room. She stepped out to get the file with their information, leaving them to her manila folders stacked on the floor and her pink afghan draped over the couch.

Brian took the opportunity to text Michael. He told himself that it would allow his husband to give last-minute advice, but he knew there was no chance of that. Michael hadn't responded to his other texts or even wish him good luck before leaving. Yet he wanted Michael to see the text and picture him sitting in a big office and making a big deal. For his own money.

"Put that away. She's coming back." Judy turned to look at the door, but nothing happened. "Where is she anyway? How can you not be ready for a pitch?"

"For a successful person like her, it's just another meeting."

"Don't let him do that to you. And don't text him if he hasn't responded."

At least I have someone. He kept this angry thought from contacting his vocal cords. He was fed up with her. But it was because they spent too much time with each other.

It was also not the truth. Ronnie had died three years ago and Brian still envied Judy's relationship with him and the thirty-two years they had together.

They turned towards the empty desk. Judy did the mouth thing she did when she worried her dentures would slip. "This is not a good sign. This lady being gone for so long I mean."

"She's harried. Overworked." Brian cupped his phone between his hand and leg.

"That tells us something about this company then, doesn't it?"

"It means she's our last chance. I didn't use every fucking vacation day to get to a dead end."

"Don't talk like that. What if she is listening to us? I wish all I had to lose was vacation time."

Brian spoke as if someone was listening in. "I'd rather no one take us on than a company that won't do things well."

"It's this or nothing." Judy put her fingers to her mouth. "You know that. Can we just sit quietly and do what it takes to get this woman to buy?"

Brian launched himself out of his chair.

"What are you doing?"

He walked around the desk. He wanted to respond with a question of his own, *Why are you at the shop before I get there and after I leave?* Instead he glanced down at Helen's monitor. "She has another appointment in ten minutes."

Judy let out a sound that sounded like a bull touching his nose to an electric fence. At the same moment, Helen opened her door

"Great view from here." Brian looked out the window with his hands on the heat register. Both women tracked him as he wandered back to his chair. "You were gone a while."

Judy leaned towards Helen. "No she wasn't."

Helen tossed a manila folder on her desk. Their folder with their correspondence askew and rumpled at the edges. Then she sat down in front of it. "Well, tell me about your product."

Brian tried to make eye contact with Judy. Judy focused on the brochure and other information that spelled out their product as Helen held them. "Abso-lutely." He took a breath. Readied his commercial voice. "Have you ever thought about the air in your bathroom? Not the smell, but the particles that create the odor. And the action of lifting the toilet lid? It reminds me of opening the doors at Starbucks. You open that first door and that second door about four feet away swings open by the vacuum created. The fact of the matter is that when you lift the toilet lid you pull up the germs and send them into the air.

"And where do they land? Everywhere. And what is the worst spot for them to land? On your toothbrush. At my household we designate a spot in the medicine cabinet that keeps them high and dry. And still someone in my house-hold sets his toothbrush behind the faucet." He looked to Judy

Judy was already talking. "And I know that these disgusting germs are in the air, but I am in a trance until I get a cup of coffee. I have a covered toothbrush holder, but I am forever forgetting to shut the lid on that thing." She raised her eyebrows and looked up to give this some sincerity.

Brian continued. "That's why we created the toothbrush garage."

Judy broke in early and took over. "You simply wave your hand near the top." She waved her hand like she was frosting a cake with her fingers. "And the top opens and uncovers your toothbrush. You then brush your teeth like normal." She mimicked brushing her teeth with an earnestness that Brian admired. "Very good," Helen responded after four interruptions thereof. the top automatically closes and protects your toothbrush all day long. get our prices down."

Let the lady with the ketchup on her blouse make her point. He willed Judy to do that. At the same time he thought how Michael would never eat anything that required ketchup. He wondered if Judy saw the glob. As they sat at her kitchen table and ate Arby's, they had discussed how successful people don't eat normal food.

It's probably too late. Judy interrupting this woman has already lost us

118

the deal. "I do want to point out that we already made 85,000 dollars in sales. Just by using the materials we have been able to procure, and assembling them in Judy's garage."

"Oh wow. I mean I see that. It's okay. I consider that my job. To take a successful product and take it to the next level. My question for you, Mr. Wilcox and you Ms. Dempsey-"

"Mrs. I'm a Mrs."

"Okay. I'm a Ms. Ms. is just an automatic thing for me."

"My husband passed," Judy said, grasping her wedding ring with her fingers. "That's all."

Brian folded his arms. *Let her call us whatever she wants.*

"No problem. Mrs. Dempsey. I am interested in working with your product. I talked to my higher ups and we can make a deal. Here's the caveat. We want-we feel-that for your company to be branded correctly, one of you will have to become a silent partner. When we go to meetings with the chain stores and such, we want just one of you. If we do an infomercial, only one of you will be on camera. You will talk about your company and your product as yours. Not me and so and so's.

Brian felt Judy's eyes on him as he sat forward in his chair. She knew his eyes narrowed when he was too upset to speak. He knew his eyes had narrowed.

"I'm afraid it's the only way we can work with your product."

"What will the other person do? Oversee the production?"

"We have people for that. We have people for everything."

Once their company had made it big, Brian saw himself at Michael's parties and his coworkers talking about his success. They might rib him about the product. They would definitely rib him about the cheesy commercials he hosted. He wanted that so that they would eat shit when he told them the financial numbers. People would respect him when he was a common household phrase just like Ron Popeil and the Pocket-Fisherman. Michael would listen and they would relate to running a huge company. He would talk to him the way he talked with the people he talked to on the phone.

"I can give you guys a few moments to choose who it will be. But I need an answer right now. Is that something one of you can do?"

"That's not reasonable." Brian felt the rumble from his cell phone. He leaned back.

"I don't have the time to be reasonable."

Judy brought her purse to her lap. Her damn purse that she took everywhere, even out to the garage to work. And what was in it? Tissue and her dead husband's asthma inhaler. "We've both worked day and night on our product. It's the only thing we have."

Brian heard the rustle of rough fabric rubbing. Helen's sleeves rubbing at the armpit as she closed their file. Brian thought of Helen's life. A husband or, more likely an ex-husband and a few awkward kids not as much responsible for the chaos each morning as Helen herself. Her job paid well and allowed her to travel.

He and Judy had the empty garage with equipment and packing materials. Nothing else. Judy was right. Each morning they turned on the lights and went to work. After their three employees went home, they did paperwork at Judy's kitchen table, a western-themed thing.

What did Judy have? A garage with equipment and her husband's powder blue mustang convertible under a car cover. The only thing she did not sell off to put in her share of the capital.

Brian wanted his own money. More importantly, Michael's friends must see his success. As a silent partner, he would only fade further into the background of Michael's interests.

He asked himself, for the first time, what Judy was doing going into any business. He asked himself, thinking the answer was just to keep busy and that would allow him to push her out.

Helen placed her hand on the closed file. "You guys did it. Not many inventors get this far."

He did not respect Helen at all. Yet it felt good to hear her say the words. Judy put her hand on Brian's arm. He juxtaposed all the things he wanted with what she wanted - to keep busy. It made him think an odd thing. *The more you have, the less you need.*

He took Judy's hand. "Meet Mr. Silent Partner."

- **Thomas Cannon**

120

Hikers in the Valley

I wish I could go back to a month and a half ago. To that safe cocoon of oblivion. I was horribly ignorant, and there is a kind of safety in that. It's easy to crave oblivion now, knowing there will never be another day of my life when I can deny or ignore what has happened.

I'm scared to return home, where my entire life was about denial. Every day I awoke with the desire to submerge myself back within sleep. To stave off reality for a little longer. While I sleep, denying myself, dark hair turns to silver on the pillow, and eyelids crease with the weight of dreams. Now there is no hiding, no safety or comfort in sleep. Every dream is a nightmare, and every morning a 5 o'clock phone call scattering a million jagged tears, like shards of broken glass, across my pillow.

The sickening plummet of the stomach, knowing this is real.

This

is

real.

~ ~ ~

While I lay dreaming, death sat on my brother's bed, night after night, conversing into the dawn, rubbing my brother's knees, his hunched shoulders. He watched blue circles grow beneath my brother's eyes. Every time my brother looked up, his eyes pleading, full of tears, death was always there to stare back at him. Death didn't do much in the way of seduction. He just sat and listened. Sat a little too close. Sat a little too long. He behaved impassively, but he was always there. After long, frustrating days he stood in the doorway, barring all exits with his sympathetic smile. Death was always the easiest one to turn to.

My brother recognized death, an old acquaintance from when he was ill with cancer. Back then, death was aloof, pacing the hospital halls. My brother was curious, even became accustomed to the soft padding of feet. But death respectfully kept his distance. One morning my brother awoke to find death standing at the window, his back to my brother, black against the light of the sun. My brother struggled through icy fog to sit up, to look closer, to see better. The light around death was dazzling, a corona; it hurt to look at death but my brother wouldn't look away, hoping death would turn around, show his face. He didn't. So for a while they gazed together in silence out the window. My brother slid backwards into sleep. When he awoke, the brilliant after-image of death was still blazing on his eyelids. His fever had broken.

Death visited my brother in the hospital when his friends wouldn't. Death was comforting in the sense that he was a constant. Perhaps when my brother got well he missed death. Perhaps my brother was secretly thrilled when, five years later, he glanced in the mirror and his eyes snagged on death's reflection. It was a sense of control, knowing he could call death to himself now.

- **Carella Keil**

Don't Come in My Store

Jeremy sat on the bench and absently stared into the street where he saw the driver of the rear-ender arguing with the driver of the rear-endee. Their misgivings were nothing like his of a half hour ago.

He hadn't gone into Maury's Music Mart with the idea of stealing a CD. He had just wanted to fill some time while his mother and sister picked out dresses for a wedding. So in he went. He wasn't even thinking about any particular music. He was just filling some time, and then it caught his eye: "Reckless Kelly was Here."

It was a boxed set with two CDs and a DVD of a live show in Houston. He had no idea Reckless Kelly had released a project like that. He looked at it. It would be so awesome to have that! He looked again. It would be pretty awesome to have the money to buy it.

The phone behind the counter rang, and Jeremy's eyes were drawn to the sound. He saw Maury turn his back to answer it, then start writing down an order. Without thinking, Jeremy pushed the boxed set under his sweater. That was easy he thought. Now I just have to get out of here.

Maury's was an old shop. It didn't have scanners by the door like the stores at the mall. It was as good as done.

He was just reaching for the door handle when Maury said, "Just a minute son. Bring that Reckless Kelly back here and put it on the counter."

Jeremy did as he was told. He wanted to apologize, or say that he wasn't really a crook, but his throat was so tight, it was all he could do to breathe. He was sweating and shaking and wondering if Maury was going to call the police.

Instead, Maury looked him straight in the eye. "Don't ever come in my store again."

That was it.

Jeremy watched the cars and tried to feel good about the fact that he wasn't busted, that nobody would ever know. Except him and Maury. But he did not feel good.

He heard his mother and sister long before he saw them in the crowded street. They were laughing at something as they pranced down the sidewalk with shopping bags and bumping into one another.

"Jeremee-ee-ee!" his mother called, waving as though they were just getting home from Europe or something. She often clowned around like that.

"Oh, Jeremy, we've had the best time shopping. It's time you had some fun. Let's get a burger at Chubby's-Hubba-Hubba."

His mother locked an arm in his, and his sister did the same on the other side. Down the sidewalk they marched to Jeremy's favorite burger joint. His mother and sister were still laughing and talking and pushing into him as they got to Chubby's and went in.

In the booth, Jeremy couldn't stop thinking about it. Chubby's-Hub-ba-Hubbah was his favorite place, and here he was. And Maury's was a place he could never go in again.

- Fred Cheney

A Drink Stand in Hamburg

His primal smile   was wary
curved eggshell cheeks   a brittle effigy
cracking   black yolk birthing instant
perhaps   it was the neo-nazi cross
tattoo on his neck   each malicious
tattoo   crocheted   across his shaved
head   a tattoo   singly as   black
teardrops worn   a war mark
against someone   with darker tint   bruised
battered   bled   possibly
he and his mate   with cheeky smirk
at me   my wife   my son
probing weak points   for a pocket
knife point   moment   at the five
to six steps isolating us   it was Sunday
in a public place   in a city center
a time for sweet Italian ice cream strolls
who would engage   past the tension
the eyes of my wife   riled   as a lioness
eeriness stirring   my neck hairs   spiked
synchronize lighthouses   triangulating
this man's tromping steps   wander inches
from our son   or was this   their joy
fabricating us   to feel weak

- **Mervyn Seivwright**

Colour Blindness

A boy called me
"Blackjack"—
I was an undefiled
seven-year-old
in an Ipswich school
sports day, thinking

this label was a layered
cage, a mental bowling ball,
knocking down my pins
of confidence
I high-wired on.
Why did he slap me

with this name,
symbolized in card games
my uncles would play?
A distraction to keep me
from running my race.
"Blackjack," stuck

in my head instead
of celebrating
my win, an echo
bell-chime ringing
under my skin,
clinging red ants

to the sweeten
rotten apple stench
they could not let go.
I still cannot let go.
My sight opened
to the darkened shroud

of my skin. A ghost
haunting this word
at moments
of mirrored reflection,

a colour marking
the crossroads, when

I started fighting
for my existence to be.

- **Mervyn Seivwright**

What You Can Take

When she woke up that last day, she decided to make up a new mythology. Nothing serious or ugly. No lightning throwing. The rose goddess, the beetle god. God of carpets, goddess of sofas and cell phones.

It was more than she could do to look out the window. So she didn't. She could tell anyway that it was sunny, which was the last straw. If you asked her.

Is there something wrong, her boyfriend asked last night. She said no, because. None of his business. She'd already broken up with him in her mind, which was where it counted.

The night before she had realized that she was free – not just from him, but from everything. She could go out right now and kiss someone or steal a car. She didn't know how to steal a car, but probably you could Google it. She could steal a car in a nice color and drive it to Arkansas, although she wasn't sure where Arkansas was. She could get all her hair cut off, or better, she could cut it herself with her mother's scissors, which were the kind the professionals used, her mother had always said.

Her boyfriend was still in bed, sleeping face down, as silent as if he were dead. Which he was, to her. He wouldn't wake up until late afternoon, unless she woke him, which she wouldn't do. Would never do again. If he had the sense to wake up she'd have broken up with him in person, but oh well.

You're a new breed of girl, the bartender had said last night when he was trying to get in her pants. Cut it out, she'd said. "New breed, I'm telling you." The woman on the next bar stool who she didn't know from god said, "New breed of woman, asshole." "New breed of asshole," she'd said, pleased to have come up with something on the fly, and they both laughed, that kind of laugh that women do when they're feeling solidarity. We're together in it, sister – that kind of laugh. They had linked arms and gone out on the dance floor and did a wild drunken dance until the other woman reeled away to the ladies.

Maybe you were supposed to remember the good times at this point, but she figured she could do that later, in the season of regret. She'd remember later that he had a nice chin and tipped too much. He tipped so much it was embarrassing TBH. The first one hundred times he kissed her his mouth was soft. Which it still was, probably.

She didn't have room in her brain for his mouth or any of that. She was making a list of concepts or beings to worship. In the new order of things. He was lying behind her on the bed as limp as a rag and meanwhile the sky was opening up, showing the start of a new world where there were no hard edges. Everything was soft there, she saw. Everything was in shades of something that would be pink except there was no word for it. There was no word for anything she was leaving behind, she was pretty sure.

- **Mary Grimm**

Paris: Lessons On Friendship

I

(The Sorbonne)

Late evening on the Left Bank. The end (so we thought) of our first day in the city. Post Basque dinner, we strolled slowly with the crowds. Full of wine. Full of Paris. Our travelers' energy was fading fast as we headed back to the hotel. He heard it first.

"What's that noise? It sounds tribal."

Heads up. We were suddenly on full alert, trying not to look too much like the tourists we were. I outpaced Ron, but then again, I hadn't flown from Honolulu to Paris in one long throw. My flight had been 3 hours shorter than his.

We threaded along a narrow street, packed with milling students and gawkers. Bored cops shared cigarettes. Spoke into the mics pinned on their flak jackets. Laughed. All while their eyes shifted, sorting out the benign from the suspicious.

We approached the heavy door and glimpsed a courtyard full of smoking dissidents. Heard the drums that had seduced us. Maybe a guitar. Maybe a flute. What could be more quintessentially Paris? Could we get in?

"Do you know where we are?" I had to raise my voice. We'd gotten separated.

"It says Sorbonne on the arch."

"The..."

Sorbonne. The real center of Paris. The natural habitat of poets, philosophers, scholars, writers, artists, the new wave, existentialism, post-modernism, and now- me. Was it asthma or ecstasy that made me gasp? For this I had traveled half the world.

We slipped around the cops (les flics) into the courtyard. Felt like infiltrators. We were infiltrators, though more benign than covert. A white banner scrawled with slogans hung across a recess. My dicey French wasn't up to translating it. No one was singing. There weren't any speakers. Things were obviously winding down.

We raised our cameras, almost in unison, trying not to be too obvious.

Cue the cast. Trying not to look at the cameras, a few guys shifted closer to one another. Shoulders were shrugged. Cigarettes were dangled. Heads were nodded. Were the drums a little louder? A cop or two dodged our lenses. Unobtrusively. Obviously we weren't just tourists. Who knew where we were from? The media? Ron in his Aussie hat looked like a real deal war photographer. My camcorder topped his Nikon, though. And I was wearing the vest. This was in the days before cellphone cameras and selfies. Our half-mast eyelids made us look blasé rather than just exhausted.

We spoke to no one. No one spoke to us. I eavesdropped, though. Didn't understand a word. I needed subtitles. And yet- and yet- the militant ennui came through loud and clear.

It didn't last long. The night finally defeated us. The demonstrators drifted away in small groups. The cops shut up shop and left. We strolled out. If we'd known how to hail a cab we would have.

"You know the little pixels that wink out when you turn off a TV? I feel like the last one…"

"Say good night, Ron."

II
(Eureka)

"I'm going to get lost today."

"Write when you find work." Ron rolled over. "Drinks at seven at the usual joint."

I left the room without a map, a clue, or hesitation.

Paris. April. Sunday morning. Les boulangeries were closed. No aroma of yeast and sugar. No chocolate or berry tarts. No baguettes. I was on my own.

The sun was well up but the streets were empty. A glitter in the gutter. A broken bottle. Clear and jagged- just like gin. And then I heard the big green street sweeper behind me. I whipped out the camera. Snapped a shot of the bottle and then the approaching truck from a low angle. Smiled at the workers. One of them waved.

My feet were my compass. I strolled down familiar/unfamiliar side streets. Discovered the Centaur- part man, part horse, part machine, standing on a plinth in front of the Swatch shop.

Shot scenes through the dusty glass of a religious goods store featuring ecclesiastical garments for those special Sundays with God. Devoured every sight, sound, and scent like a glutton. Hoarded raw materials for my memories.

Suddenly, the bells rang out from St. Suplice. Famous St. Suplice- the multi-storied, double-steepled dame of the square. Their deep, tolling sounds vibrated through my whole body just as I was snapping pigeons on a massive fountain. I sat with them waiting for the next outburst. The mass of the church awed and disturbed me.

"Why do people feel they have to trap god into stone forts with elaborate windows? Are they trying to crush him down to their size? And, while I'm at it- what is the meaning of life? What am I meant to do here? What must I accomplish to get life right?"

Then- epiphany, revelation, shock and, perhaps, awe. An answer. The Answer. The one I'd been searching for my whole adult life. I had to come to the City of Light to hear it.

"Nothing. This is it. This is all there is."

The prophets of existentialism seeped into my soul. They freed me from my heavy American guilt. I preached it to the birds, but they knew it already. They were, after all, Parisian pigeons. I had to share it instantly. In English. With Ron, obviously.

I retraced my steps, but the streets looked different. Had I passed that carved doorway on my way? That graffiti? That garden gate? I heard the rattle of bistro cups. Paris was waking up.

Eventually I found Ron at our corner cafe observing the sleepy tourists. Drinking coffee. Eating croissants. Just that.

"You'll never guess what!"

"You're back from the ice shelf, Shackelton! You didn't get lost after all."

"I have nothing to live for! Nothing! This is it!"

He choked.

"And?"

"Life is sweet! Pass the chocolate, pal."

III
(Standards)

Night in Montmartre. I stood, one foot propped against a wall, in front of a grocery store waiting for Ron. Crowds drifted to and fro. Self-conscious young girls. Old travelers with maps. It was tourist season.

"Voulez vous coucher?" he asked. A tall African fellow, beautiful as the night. Jeans. T shirt. Wide sly smile. White teeth.

I swiveled my head. Was he talking to me? He was talking to me.

"Pardonnez moi?"

"Tu veux coucher…?"

Did I want to…? Really? Bed? Sex, even?

"Non, monsieur. Mais merci por asking." I answered breathlessly. So American. Wide-eyed. Beaming.

Ron exited the store just then with a basket of ripe strawberries. M. Coucher evaporated.

"You'll never guess," I breathed.

"I heard," he answered. Laughed. Hugged me in my innocence.

"Was that what I thought it was?" My French was dicey, but I knew that question, ofcourse. From the song.

"It was."

We walked the late night hills eating the berries. Late night but crowded. Late night but wide awake. Late night washed with neon and streetlamps. Late night down to Pigalle. We dug out our passes and descended into the metro. We changed trains two stops later and felt ourselves Parisian. The train was nearly full.

131

Then- he stood across the aisle, facing us. Handsome, not to put too fine a point on it. Magnetic. A standing member of the proletariat. I glanced at him, then stared. And, at once, he did, too. We broke the gaze. Looked again. Blushed- both of us. I grinned. He grinned. Vavin station came up too soon. I fairly skipped up the stairs.

"You'll never guess..." I began.

"I saw," Ron answered, laughing hard. My best friend.

I clapped my hands. "I just realized! No woman ever has to be alone in Paris."

"Unless, of course, she has standards," he observed. "Which you don't."

"Which, apparently, I don't," I agreed.

IV
(A Taste of the Sahara)

"I've got a surprise for you. Meet me at Sacre Coeur at 6. And bring your appetite."

"You're such a romantic, Ron."

"For all the good it does me."

From the Basilica we descended to little Africa- Chateau Rouge in the shadow of Montmartre. He'd been nosing around there for a couple of days, picking up knicknacks, eating up the food and the atmosphere like a glutton. That was the difference between us. I was Paris, he was Casablanca.

His surprise was in a hole-in-the-wall, off-the-beaten track kind of cafe. No sign out front. No recognizable ambiance to speak of.

Half a dozen guys hung out at formica tables. Smoking. Drinking coffee. Scowling. Ron strode in. They went dead silent. A big guy came out of the back room and signaled him back. Like he'd been expecting him. Why? I hung outside the door looking around for other women. None. I stepped back. Scanned the shops across the street. Ron returned and escorted me in.

The back room was big and dim. Like a warehouse. But- white tablecloths on the tables. Candles, even. Menus. Unexpected class. I ordered couscous and lamb. He ordered something more exotic. No wine. It wasn't that kind of joint. He'd eaten lunch out front before and found out about the hidden secret elegance over a couple of falafel.

Ten minutes into the wait, sipping our goblets of water, there was a knock on the big metal door across from us. No one answered it. A couple of the guys from out front looked back. Another knock. This time the front room crowd drifted closer to the door. I began to think of exit strategies. They were between us and the street.

The third time the knocking started, our host came out from the kitchen and stood conferring with a couple of the front room crowd. They looked at each other. Worried, I thought. My imagination kicked into overdrive.

I had visions of plaid scarves and machine guns. Of jeeps parked at the door. Sand. Scimitars. I was an infidel, inappropriately dressed. How much of me would the tablecloth cover? Ron leaned forward on his elbows. Fascinated. Unflappable

Then- action. The host pulled back the heavy iron bar. The front room crowd backed up. He opened it slowly, slowly- and then- the cat walked in. Like a king. Meowed.

They laughed and drifted away. I breathed again.

"Nice floor show, pal. Thanks. I might write about it some day."

V

(Dead and Alive)

Noon in Montparnasse. After a late night. A very late night. An early morning/ late night night. A night that ended with bottles of wine from the corner store. While Ron perused the shelves for unfamiliar blends, I grabbed the cheapest bottle near the front door. The equivalent of $1 for a liter of pretty decent (to my untutored palate) stuff. Many cuts above rotgut.

"Meet you for drinks at six?"

We were both shouldering our cameras, shrugging on our vests, and checking our francs and metro tickets. Unconsciously doing our best Robert Capra and Lee Miller imitations.

"The usual spot?"

He laughed. More like his signature giggle.

"Look at us. We're in Paris and we already have a usual spot!"

Outside, he headed left toward the gardens and I went right, past famous cafes cum tourist traps. On the same streets the expats had haunted. Would the boulevard be so magic if I hadn't seen all the jazz age pictures, listened to the jazz age jazz, steeped myself in jazz age expat literature?

I stopped for a sandwich (ham and cheese on a baguette. Jambon et fromage. Tres cosmopolitan, though I was shocked by the lack of lettuce and tomato that would have completed an American version.) And Perrier. Hardly Hemingway fare.

Then- the gates of the cemetery Montparnasse. Where to start? I grabbed a map from the kiosk just inside the front gate.

It oozed fame. Not that I cared about the remains of the rich and famous, though I was suitably impressed when I ran across them, of course. Sartre and de Bouvier. Baudelaire. Duras. Dreyfus. Man Ray. I was in it for the art. The place was a free sculpture park. The pieces were all homage and remembrance. They weren't just about themselves. There were three people in every statue- the artist, the audience, and the dead.

A woman's body pushed up against a flat gravestone as a grieving lover stood next to it. A silver and glass bird glittered in the sun. A horse/man/machine hybrid stood guard over its creator's grave. Baudelaire's demon leered from atop a plinth. All thought-provoking- and great photo ops.

I ignored my aching back when I discovered another section of the cemetery surrounded by a high rock wall with a single barred gate. There! Brancusi's "Kiss"! A marital bed complete with (a fully clothed) industrialist and his wife! A prostrate nude draped over a rock! More, more, more. Then- I was thirsty. I was hungry. Was it time to go back? I didn't have a watch.

It was time. I could feel it as I retraced my steps. I found the gate at last. Locked. No one was around. A high wall I couldn't climb. I was unfazed.

"I can sleep here tonight. It's quiet. The ground is flat. These high walls must keep it safe. After all, the dead have been sleeping here for ages."

I was turning back when the guard arrived. Outside the gate. Rattling her keys.

"We are closed, madam."

How did she know I spoke English?

Me. Smiling. "And I am locked in."

Time passes fast when you're among the dead.

Then- the usual spot was crowded.

"You'll never guess where I've been."

"I assume it was good. You missed cocktails. I had to drink yours."

Alas, Ron is dead now and I am old. Which is the only alternative to dead.

- **Patti Cassidy**

134

Law of Attraction

I'd never believed in anything scientific evidence couldn't prove, but since the breakup, I was reaching. My love for Sadie was so strong it made me believe in the unbelievable.

"No." Emphatically said the palm reader when asked if Sadie and I would get back together.

"Are you sure though? My hands are more crackly than normal. Maybe you're missing a line."

Madame Hilda squeezed my hand tight in annoyance, but she took another look. "I see traveling in your future. A lot of money. Two healthy babies… And what seems like a rare disease where the only side effect is feeling fully refreshed after only a couple of hours of sleep. No Sadie though."

"Sadie loves to travel. And she sleeps very little, which is why she's so cranky all the time."

Sadie left me three months ago for a hunky accountant. I had been window shopping for wedding rings when she left, waiting for the right moment. I found the perfect ring yesterday.

"I need a second opinion. Do you have a tarot deck?" I asked.

"It's thirty dollars, but for you, I'll do forty."

"Anything to know when Sadie is coming back!" I said removing some crumpled-up bills from my pocket.

I am told what came next would terrify anyone who understood tarot, but luckily, I didn't. I just wanted somebody to say the exact opposite of what my family and friends, and therapists, had been saying. Instead, the cards I picked were:

"The ten of swords. This means you will likely suffer some unwelcome surprise in the near future. It's not my job to guess, but if I had to, I'd say the surprise will be that Sadie isn't coming back."

"Or that it will just take her longer than expected. Maybe another week or two, I know how much she hates being in the city for the winter."

"Your second card is the Devil—"

"Is it because Sadie is coming back and things will get pretty hot and heavy?"

"No. The Devil is a warning card. A warning that you're being self-destructive."

The last card ended up being the Death card, which felt very cliché. But I was hopeful it meant the death of the accountant.

"If you carry anything with you out of here, please let it be this, SHE IS NOT COMING BACK," pleaded the fortuneteller.

"Is that really what you see in the future?"

"No. That's what I see on her Instagram," she said revealing her phone from underneath the desk and flaunting a photo of a woman that looked a little like Sadie making out with a sexy CPA in the Bahamas.

I tipped the lady because I'm not letting my depression change the good person I am. But all she said was a bunch of bullshit, which is precisely why I don't believe in this sort of thing.

- Gustavo Barbur de Melo

"A Frog of a Railroad To Become a Prince of a Park"

(Front page headline in the *New York Times,* about the High Line, 2008)

The West Side Elevated Line, overtaken by time—
refrigerated trucks and dead pedestrians—
abandoned, decrepit, overgrown.

Then some peasant girl or architect
kissed the frog on Gansevoort Street and 13th, where later
Bill's Bar and Burger would serve brews to tourists and locals,

and like the Promenade Plantee, the freight line rose,
tracks preserved, weeds cherished,
blood twig dogwood and bottle brush buckeye co-existing

with witch hazel, winged sumac, and wild purslane,
the urban and the natural entwined, artfully
made to look unrehearsed.

Multi-dimensional art, "sculpture" in the old parlance,
surprises every year—sometimes fountains
spouting from blacked-out eyes,

sometimes splashes of color on walls,
always a point-of-view
urging us to think while we count

the words scatter as we walk—
Arabic, Bengali, Afrikaans, Japanese—
the global village as Babylon.

- **Shaheen Dil**

Henny

I couldn't believe it -- Ginger had gotten her chicken on the radio. I don't mean that it was sitting on top of the radio receiver, laying eggs or something. I mean actually on the air waves, clucking away her famous cluck-cluck song.

I was sitting there in the living room, late Sunday morning. I'd made myself breakfast, or as Ginger used to say, 'something like breakfast' -- saltines with butter and jam and a cup of coffee -- only I was out of butter so I used Crisco. I'd finished eating and was sitting on the sofa with an ice cube wrapped in an old sock on my forehead to cool me down, when I realized I missed having someone to talk to.

When Ginger left a few weeks ago, with her dog, her frying pans, her dresses, and her prize chicken, I was happy for the peace and quiet, 'cause Ginger was always talking, or her dog was always barking, and she was always getting her chicken to cluck-cluck that song she'd play on the Ukulele.

But that Sunday morning, I was starting to miss all the noise, so I turned on the radio, thinking it'd be like someone was talking to me. And if I wanted, I could always talk back to the speaker. But there was Ginger, speaking to the whole world, saying "The next song Henny's going to sing for us is called 'Ain't going to lay no more.'" And up went the ukulele strings followed by Ginger yodeling, then Henny's clucks on the chorus. It was like they were back in the house again, Ginger and Henny, and everything back to normal. Only I had a sour feeling in my stomach -- from my breakfast, or from what I drank the night before, or from hearing them now chatting with the DJ on the radio, talking about their performance next week at a country western club in Nashville, a hundred miles from here.

The DJ asked Henny how she liked being on the road, and Henny clucked an answer, which Ginger translated, saying, "She says it's better than crossing it."

The audience laughed, which is when I realized she was on a live show already.

I got up then and turned off the station. "Welp," I said to myself, just to hear a voice, "guess I should get out of the house. Go out and get some groceries, so I can make myself a proper breakfast tomorrow."

I put on my jacket and found my truck keys, as I started to make a list in my head: bread, milk, butter, and a dozen eggs.

- **Nathan Long**

How to Grow a Baby
(when your uterus is covered in fibroids and your husband has left you.)

Step 1.
Research IVF and sperm donors. Learn that you will never be able to afford them on your salary, especially since your husband has left you and taken you off his health insurance.

Step 1b.
Research adoption. Learn that not only will you not be able to afford this either, but single mothers with mental health issues are not at the top of the list, as far as adoption agencies go.

Step 2.
Ask your high school friend's younger brother to help you get on the dark web. (He will proposition you, turn him down. He'll help you either way because he thinks you smell good.)

Step 2b.
Consider buying a baby on the dark web, learn it is even more expensive than a legal baby. Stumble upon a forum for infertile witches and create your own hodge-podge ritual that will absolutely spell either b-a-b-y or disaster. Ignore all warnings, especially the ones regarding closed practices.

Step 3.
Plant a ring of ginger approximately 4 feet wide in a sunny spot in your garden. (Usually, a lot of sunlight means a lot of moonlight, too, but best to check it the night before you plant. Just in case.) In the middle of the ginger, bury an egg. The egg should be pre-rubbed with van-van oil and rubbed clockwise on a pregnant belly 9 times. (If you don't know any pregnant people, a food baby is fine for this step. Eat a box of powdered donuts and 3 microwaved bean burritos before you do the clockwise rubbing. Tell yourself it is the thought that counts.)
Note: *In the case of apartment living, consider using a bourbon barrel. See ap-pendix for specs and nutritional supplement suggestions.*

Step 4.
Cut your palm with the gardening shears because you left the kitchen knife you sanitized inside the house. Over the soil where your precious hopes will germinate, sprinkle blood from your clenched fist. Forget to clean your cut and watch your hand get mildly infected. Consider whether you are ready for a baby when you can't even take care of yourself.

Step 5.

Water daily. Completely freak out when a woman on YouTube with a sundress and a straw hat tells you that over-watering is one of the quickest ways to kill your garden. Stick tampons in the soil between the ginger that has sprouted and the empty spot in the middle that has not. Cry the entire next day when it rains an inch and a half and almost kills your ginger.

Step 6.

Consult your notes. Realize what you are missing. Consider asking your high school friend's younger brother, but immediately dismiss it. He's too obvious when he sniffs your hair. Anyways, best for someone with no attachments here. Find a decently attractive man in a bar across town. Convince him to come to yours (not hard to do, you still look great for your age, since you haven't got a 'mom bod') and insist he follow you in separate cars. (Don't forget this part!) Make sure and use a condom. Lie back and think of England. Afterwards, while he's snoring into the cold side of your bed, fish the condom out of the little waste-basket tucked under the bedside table and sprinkle the contents into the barren soil between the ginger plants you nursed back to health.

Note: *He isn't sleeping. He will see you fishing out the condom. He is a loud breather, bad adenoids. He will think you are married and sneak out. Secretly consider how nice it would be if he was in a terrible drunk driving accident on the way home. A dead father is probably less emotionally scarring than an absent father. Consider that you could lie, though. He doesn't have to be dead. Already, you've forgotten his name. Feel a bit better. Tell yourself a mother would do any-thing for their child.*

Step 7.

Try not to obsess. Try not to overwater it, or underwater it. Admire its pretty leaves when they finally start to show. Try not to drag an umbrella out when the sun is very bright. Cut your palm with the pre-sanitized kitchen knife, over the same spot. No need for more than one scar. Squeeze your clenched fist close to the soil, under the soft green leaves, like lambs ear. Bury your hair where the ginger was; after you've dug it up and the bulbous roots made you think about round little baby legs and plump little baby toes. Ignore that it falls out in clumps, your once-lustrous auburn locks. Ignore the bruises that pop up constantly, like your skin is too weak to keep anything out, or to keep your blood in. Tell yourself, I am growing a baby, spiritually. It is taxing on one's body.

Step 8.

You will know when it is time. The leaves will start to yellow at the edges. You may get the urge to push. Dig with your hands, in your nightgown, under the moonlight. Follow the stalk, still strong and pulsing with life, down into the earth, much deeper than the egg was buried. When you are in the dirt up to your elbow, you will feel a soft yet solid thing in the loam. Grasp it tightly. Brace your heels on something. Pull with all your might. This will be difficult. You may be very enfeebled at this point. The baby will breach the surface like a shark, or a cicada. Be ready to catch it. Even in your weakened state, you must be ready. You're a mother now, after all.

Step 9.

Make sure its mouth is cleared of dirt. A healthy baby is a hollering baby. A good loud wail at birth is music to your ears. Ignore the tendrils that cling to the woodsy, textured skin. Lovingly count the fingers and toes that elongate and split and splinter into long, tangled bunches of roots. Be enamored no matter what number you come up with. Coo into the divots on the side of its head, most likely its ears. Do not concern yourself with gender. It may become discernible later. Do not concern yourself with those sharp, thorny teeth. They will not be an issue since this baby will not need to be nursed. Consider, that they are kind of cute.

Note: *To repeat, this child will not need to be nursed. Do not, under any circumstances, attempt to breastfeed your home-grown baby. It may attempt to root or nuzzle. Your breasts may fill with milk. (Click this link for a tutorial on wrapping your breasts to cease milk production.) You should still not, under any circumstances, attempt to breast-feed.*

Congratulations on your new baby!

- **Rachael Magruder**

Un mensaje de los Apus
A Message from the Mountains

Sweet woodruff star-bursts upward along the shores of Cottonwood Creek. In
this dusty, high valley, here is some green, *algo verde,* to nourish my soul.
    Quenching a thirst I had become accustomed to,
          hope drinks deep.

Through the Cottonwood's branches I glimpse the 14,000 foot
          Apus to the east.
Those Cloud Catchers' snow pack continually nourishing
         those of us at her feet,
sustaining life in the absence of rain.

     Mountain Spirits
Sangre de Cristos a los conquistadores and those of us in their *camino* Navajo's
Sísnájíni - black and white sash belt - Mother Earth's sacred waist band. I want
      to follow their *camino.*

     Harsh Beauty abounds
Spring winds so fierce they toss my neighbor's trampoline through fields
of *chamisa.*
    When She roars loudly enough,
      even we busy beings have no choice but to stop
       and bow to Her Force.

Everywhere reminders of our smallness
   in trees growing from sheer rock
   in frogs dormant beneath the caked dirt
Some say they can live up to three years beneath that dirt
      others say we don't know how long.

   They are not as impatient as I for rain.

   Life, resilient, perseveres here.

As our human world persists,
   burdened by grief, fear, exhaustion
   exploited, stressed and sick
unprecedented chicanery, violence, and divisiveness
      filling our living rooms.

Outside, the *Apus* whisper:

 Dig deeper, child. You too have this force within you.

- Joan Gauscheman

Out of the Rubble

I was born in a building destroyed by a Russian missile, apparently just before it struck. A man crawled into the wreckage to rescue me and held me up over his head with one hand when he worked his way back out. For a day he was regarded as a hero. Then a doctor at the hospital where I was taken criticized him in an interview for making a self-serving gesture. He should have cradled me, not hoisted me up into the air. When I was six a neighborhood friend, a girl the same age, showed me an internet video of the man with me in his hand.

"That's you. My mommy found it."

"No, it's not."

"You're adopted."

"I know that."

"This is where they got you. You were born in the building that got blown up."

"Stop saying that."

My father had told me he was working for UN relief and asked his supervisor to go to the hospital with him and pretend they were married. The hospital had been hit, too, and was evacuating. It surrendered me to them without hesitation. Wartime fate, he said.

"I already had a return ticket to the States and brought you home."

Home meant New Jersey where I blocked memory of that video for a long time. I did not want to know about myself if it meant being that infant. I preferred to believe I was one child under the rubble and another child out of it. We didn't talk to one another. The child in the rubble had nothing to say.

My parents divorced when I was twelve in part because my father defended every bad thing I did. I had a half-brother who left with her. That didn't turn me around. The odd thing about an adolescent's troublemaking is that she sees no connection between what she did wrong in June and what she does wrong in August. She doesn't connect misdeeds the way adults do. She sees no patterns, ominous narratives about what she's becoming bore her, what's there to talk about? Caught cheating in school? Caught shoplifting? Reckless sex? Drinking herself unconscious? Drugs? It all burns off like mist on a pond in the morning sun. Disconnections in time are matched by disconnections in space. Life is here and now until a week or two later it's somewhere else.

Something happened when I was sixteen that most people would consider trivial. My father and I were sitting on the back deck during a false spring with coastlines of snow in the shadows under the railings.

"If I were the guy then that I am now, I wouldn't have the balls to go to Ukraine," he said.

He never spoke to me in the frank, pained tone of voice he used—this was new—or talked about anyone's balls or called someone an asshole. I realized he had given up on trying to protect me from myself.

"I felt that I was abandoning Ukraine at the worst moment, so I said to myself, What about that baby? No one's claimed her. Go get her and take her with you. My boss had made it from Cameroon to Paris and changed her life, so she'd try anything. She was one they handed you to. I didn't get you until we were in the street. I couldn't do something like that now. I wouldn't have the balls."

When he said that, it was like a bird hitting a window, me the bird and me the window. I was terrified that he was going to go on and say, "I had the balls then, but thank God I don't anymore because look at how you turned out." He didn't say, but I did. Then and there I collided with myself. For the first time the infant in the rubble had something to say: I was on my own.

Thoughts of now brought on thoughts of then. I couldn't stop them. One thought was that the sudden destruction of a building explained so much about me. I imagined being born one second and the next second the missile hitting the building and the second after that my mother dying and the second after that the man holding me up above his head. Birth, missile, death, rescue. Were they connected, or weren't they? And I would insert new seconds within the old seconds—the second in which the man realizes there is an infant alive in the rubble, the second in which he gets his hand on it—but it almost wrecked me trying to fuse them together. I had lived a life of full stops, then on to the next one. But here my father was doing something else. He was using himself then to understand himself now, confessing how much it hurt not to have the balls to be brave anymore, which took guts, guts I realized I never had.

For the next few years my fight with myself got worse. I didn't want to hear that baby crying. But by my mid-twenties, almost despite myself, I had earned a college degree—two, in fact—and found a way to make a living. I never put things right with my ex-mother, but I no longer gave my father trouble, and I began thinking about the man who rescued me. Had the Russians eventually killed him, too? Radopolis, where I was born, had been rebuilt the same way dozens of other Ukrainian cities and towns were rebuilt. Built anew, I should say, wholly new and repopulated, no doubt, by more newcomers than survivors. But I decided to search for him and see if that would bring then and now together.

On arrival in Radopolis I immediately wanted to leave. The entire city was shrink-wrapped in a kind of pristine nakedness with its perfectly straight lines and perfectly smooth surfaces. Tragedy wasn't its gestalt. What war?

I spent much of my first day in the hotel coffee shop, checking train and flight schedules and only occasionally going outside for a walk trying to convince myself to stay. On the second day the hotel concierge, an older man in a gray sack of a suit, told me he remembered that there had been a man who had pulled a newborn out of the rubble during the war but had no idea who he was or how to locate him. He suggested I talk to an elderly shopkeeper, who was into everything and always had been. She seemed to take me for a gold digger looking to lay hands on hidden family assets. "Are you saying you were that baby?" she asked. I said no, not at all. I was a journalist, trying to learn what people remembered thirty years later. She sent me to the headmaster of a secondary school. He couldn't see me, but his secretary passed word that he thought a man who worked for a British bank might be the one I was looking for. He was the head of the IT section. I reached him on the phone and said I was looking into rescue efforts during the war.

"Oh, that... I don't like to talk about that," he said, irritated.

"Perhaps if we could meet face-to-face, you would feel more comfortable."

"What can I tell you? I did rescues. Then I fought. Bad times."

"Did you ever pull anyone out of collapsed buildings?"

"Sure, we found people alive."

"Do you remember any?"

He said maybe, but one day wiped out the next. Who wanted to remember it all? I said my problem was that so few original residents had returned to Radopolis, and my project was oral history, firsthand testimony, actual experience. Finally, he said all right, just not at his office or in a cafe or restaurant, nowhere public. Come to his apartment. I hesitated over that but agreed.

His apartment was just like the new Radopolis: no cracks in the walls, no photographs of family members, no memorabilia, no icons, a big TV screen, a few pieces of furniture, everything spotless, as if the dust of time floated elsewhere to settle. In contrast he was the old Radopolis, a jowly, grizzled, old church of a man with swags of wrinkles beneath his eyes who seemed to have had a talk with himself and received me with a kind of forced, not wholly sincere, courtesy, offering me tea and biscuits and a candle on the dining nook table where we sat. I knew right away, not through his likeness to the video of my rescuer but through an urgent conviction that he was the man I sought.

"I'm not just a kind of journalist-historian," I said.

"What are you then?"

"I'm an orphan from Ukraine. I grew up in States."

This aroused him. He cast me a quick, hawkish look. "Maybe I can see that. You could be from Ukraine."

"I am, and I have to admit it's taken a lot for me to come find you."

"Why?"

"I think you may have rescued a newborn once."

"Oh, that," he said, appearing to brace himself, the nostrils in his big, blunt nose widening along with his murky pupils. "Why do you ask about that?"

"Because I think I am the newborn you may have rescued."

He smiled the way you smile when you've embarrassed yourself and would like to find a way to minimize what you've done, toss it off. "Yes? Wouldn't that be something? Maybe, who knows?"

"I know I was born in a building here hit by a Russian missile."

"How do you know that?"

"My father told me. He adopted me after he saw the story in the news."

146

"Your father?"

"He worked for UN relief here."

I studied him as he considered this, looking at him not just for his reaction but for resemblance to the young man in the photo displaying the infant. I saw none. He looked more like the rubble the young man had been posing on.

"Some vodka?" he asked.

"No thank you. I don't drink."

"Just a little?"

"Can't. I'm an alcoholic."

This disturbed him. He seemed to have some personal concern for me and asked if I minded him drinking. I said no. He helped himself to a bottle of vodka and poured a shot in his tea.

"So, you think you maybe could be that kid?"

"Yes, and I wonder if you know anything about me."

He shook his head ambiguously. I couldn't tell if that meant yes or no and decided I needed to push further into the story. A mistake.

"And I wonder why you held me up like that."

"Hold you up like what?"

"Over your head. A doctor criticized you for it."

"Him? What did he know?"

"What should he have known?"

Suddenly, he was very angry. "Nothing. The bastard wasn't from here."

How many thousands of times had I wondered if I was going to discover something I didn't want to discover? I wondered that now. I worried he was going to ask me to leave. To prolong the encounter, I said maybe I would like some vodka in my tea, too.

"Hell, no. If you're alcoholic, I'm not going to give you vodka."

The bad girl in me wasn't pleased. "Oh, come on."

"No."

"Then tell me why you did that."

He grew flushed. What I couldn't see looking at the hard surfaces of the rebuilt city I could see in the loose skin beneath his eye sockets and the tension in his lips.

"I thought my brother was out there watching us work, and I wanted him to see I had his baby. But he wasn't there, he was out fighting."

I don't know how to explain realizing that would make him my uncle, but he was the kind of man who wasn't anyone's anything.

"I gave the baby over to the ambulance. Next thing I heard he was killed that same day. So, our family was in the rubble, and he was gone, and that doctor made me look like a fool. Forget the rescue team. I started fighting myself." Once he started talking, he rushed on. He said he had no pictures of anyone in his family and had to work to recall their faces. "It's like they never existed. That was our building. I just wanted to get into it and save them, but it was only the baby.

I heard it crying, and I squeezed in and got it by the ankle. That's when I realized it was Malik's. His wife was the one pregnant in that building. I called to her. She didn't call back. My mother and sister and father and uncle, none of them called back. I worked my way out and when I could stand up, I lifted the baby so Malik could see at least there was something, but he wasn't there. He was being killed and then that doctor says I was an idiot, holding a naked baby up in the cold like that. It made me mad. Everything made me mad. Pretty soon there wasn't even a city to defend anymore. When we won, I passed back through here—it's all gone. The Brits give me a scholarship to study IT, but I can't settle there. Those were the terms. Must return to rebuild. Where? So here I am. It's not where I came from, but it's where I am."

By now he had the war all over his face. I tried to ask a few questions about his family, but he shook his head violently. Anna, my mother's name was Anna, he said. Malik and Anna. Forget the others, he didn't want to talk about them. He was not to acknowledge he was my uncle, either, even to reject me. He was too resentful that I had brought things back to him he wanted to keep buried. The dead were his people, not me. Somehow I found the nerve to say I had one more thing to ask: Would he take me to the spot where the building had been? He muttered that he never went there, but he used his cell phone to pull up a map of the city and showed me where to go. Beyond that, we were over. It was like a parting between two people who don't understand how they became involved in the first place. You say goodbye, he says goodbye, and that's really it.

A pinkish office building occupied the spot where I had been born. I stood across the street from it reaching for what was no longer there and discovered I was okay with that. What wasn't there was in me. It was too cold to linger long.

- **Robert Earle**

Shut Your Piehole!

she said tapping her toe, each tap
like a sewing needle stuck in me.
I blinked, already forgetting
our cattery in Green Valley, land
sliced wide open by the Green River.
"Turn around, traitor!" I complied.
"I saw the two of you together."
Like a ball-pin hammer, her fist
struck the small of my back. *Its over*
I thought. *My fault. My mistake.*
"Sorry," I eked out as she stomped
out the front door laughing
into the rain, raindrops sizzling
every sidewalk inch. Her car
splashed every bubbling puddle before
darting into mist down our street.
I walked off, my cold hands pocketed.
I only stopped once, to touch
a glistening raindrop on a filament
of a spiderweb, watched
it vibrate throughout the design
but the weaver was like air,
she was absent, nothing left caught there,
not even the muffled sound
of a spider mummified in spider-silk.

- **Mario Duarte**

Bicameral Poem on the Occasion of the Most Recent Elections

1.   Rehearsals

For the word no longer resonate,
its form now repeated mercilessly
in Russia, or in other territories
too long occupied, when you go
on a walk among trees or during
a prayer you might have raised,
look out on the current night
at the worlds we know
to be gaseous, crushing, dead,
and consider

that the rehearsal matters.
Maybe the vote, the prayer,
maybe the more we do
matters, not in charts, trends, or points,
but for the grip on the fantasy, the one known path
to realms beyond the occupier's dream.

In certain forms of aphasia,
standing at shore, though you cannot say
what you have heard
listening at night, after sirens,
voices calling across streets,
you continue this practice, return,
in this arch of the unattainable, to those shores
for the light, because if you see it, hear it, maybe
smell it, maybe then it's closer, maybe realized.

2.   Party Mode

The fascism of the corporation waves behind your flags,
calls to a duty-bound forgetfulness born of board rooms,
ahistoricity in memos and off-white reams of accounts
officially recognized after
the surrender, the first act
of fiction required of you.

But you will never, though promised
somewhere in all those reams, find the
homeland of your expectations, six
figure salary to match the magistrates, or
enough vacation time
to move away,
enough of anything ever again,

not when the arrangement here begs
and differs and will finally part your ways
between here and the drying of
the last rivers used to navigate.

- Thomas Allbaugh

The Ledger

Jerry sped away from the city with the herd of commuters on the Interstate in his pickup truck. Eric Clapton's guitar licks, slightly muted by the whoosh of the full-on air conditioner, tickled his mind as the stress and details of his workday began to fade.

He spotted the welcoming Coyle-family barn ahead, its red paint faded to an anemic pink. He sighed unconsciously; his exit was coming up. Soon he would be in the quiet sanctuary of 'the farm.' That was how he thought of his place—a rectangular five-acre plot of land with a desiccated apple orchard and a single-story, wooden clapboard two-bedroom house in the middle. It was his retreat. After the divorce, he had bought it with his half of the settlement.

He turned off the highway and into his driveway, a hundred-yard-long stretch of dirt road. As he approached the house, he saw Lisa come out carrying something. She opened the passenger door of her car. He parked against the side of the house and went over to her. She was tightening the seat belt around one of her rubber plants. Boxes, plastic bags and clothes had already been packed into the back.

"What are you doing?" he said.

Lisa looked at him sadly as she closed the door. "I'm sorry, Baby. I can't take it anymore."

He frowned in concern as he went to her, trying to take her into his arms. "C'mon, Honey, what are you talking about?"

She pulled away from him "Do you know that he shit his pants today?"

"I'm sorry," Jerry said.

She glared at him, then her face softened and she looked toward the house. "He got it all over the couch. This is not the first time I've had to clean up his messes." She looked back at Jerry, a sad smile on her face. "I can't do it anymore, Baby. I have to leave. I'm sorry."

Lisa got in the car and started it.

"Roll your window down, will you?" he said.

She shook her head and waved him back. She drove slowly down the driveway. He watched in a state of shock until she turned onto the Interstate. He sighed and went inside the house.

Dad was sitting in his electric wheelchair at the dining room table, reading his mail. "I always thought she'd leave you," he said. "I'm surprised she lasted as long as she did."

Jerry seethed. His father couldn't even see that his endless accidents, caused more by his stubborn refusal to accept his limitations, than by his infirmities themselves, had made her leave. It wasn't due to any lack of moral strength in her.

"Is that right?" was all Jerry could safely say. He needed to calm down, to think, or he'd say something he'd regret. He started toward his bedroom, the familiar garment of anger and depression falling over and around him. Maybe after he got things cleaned up he could go for a bike ride and work it out, he thought hopefully.

"Don't forget about my appointment tomorrow," his father called after him.

"What?"

"My ortho appointment."

"Oh, shit! What time?"

"Nine."

Jerry sighed. "Okay." He immediately began thinking of what kind of excuse he could give them at work. He'd already run out of vacation days.

~ ~ ~

Jerry drove faster than usual as he headed to work after dropping Dad off at home after his doctor visit. He turned the radio on to the country music station. An old, sappy song lamenting the passing of 'Mamma' and 'Papa' played. Jerry thought about Dad. Eighty-nine. He wasn"t going to be around forever. But it seemed he took up more and more of Jerry's time every year, with his almost-weekly visits to the doctors and his occasional medical emergencies. Once he was gone, Jerry could start living his own life again. But when would that be?

The thought brought a flush of guilt. Jerry tried to dismiss it. What the hell was wrong with thinking about his own damn self once in a while? He thought of Lisa and how much he missed her already. She'd been a real find and they got along really well, and she"d been kind and helpful to his father too, something which was not her job or responsibility. She had just 'stepped up,' as people say. But even she had her breaking point. He doubted he'd ever find another woman willing to move in and live with him and Dad.

Jerry parked behind the office and got out of the truck. The day's heat and humidity had already reached its uncomfortable peak. As he headed for the entrance, he thought about how he might have a tough time finding a woman—period—given how old and out-of-shape he was getting. He was fifty-nine, with a steadily growing paunch. He'd kept it at bay for a long time by riding his bike—a Trek hybrid that he loved as much as a man could love a machine. Eight gears, 24 speeds, and when he got it rolling out on the country blacktop, he felt like a thirty-year old again. But it was getting harder and harder to find the time to do that now.

At the office, Jerry spent most of the morning in Dave Taylor's cubicle trying to fix his computer which had been crashing almost every day. Jerry was the IT technician for the Memphis branch of the State's Bureau of Labor. Taylor's machine was brand new and Jerry himself had loaded all the software on it and tested it. It just didn't make sense. As Jerry ran a scan, Taylor watched him sullenly. The office manager's attractive secretary, Bernice, appeared at the entrance to the cubicle. "Good Morning, guys"

"Morning," Jerry said.

Taylor nodded.

Bernice looked at Jerry. "Mister Jefferson wants to see you."

Jerry nodded. "Okay." He wondered what was going on. Jefferson rarely called him in to his office. He turned to Taylor. "Don't touch the keyboard or turn it off. I'll be right back."

Taylor glowered at him like an overly aggressive teen forced to get out of his bumper-car at the fair.

Jerry followed Bernice. They passed Makmoud Majif who was leaning over the divider that separated his cubical from Trevor Kennedy's, the redneck.

"Trump no good," Makmoud was saying while shaking his head, "no good!"

"And I already told you a dozen times," said Trevor in his distinctive twang, "I didn't vote for him, but he *is* our president!"

Jerry acknowledged the two men with a nod before going into Jefferson's office. Bernice sat down across from Jefferson, looking down as she began swiping her finger across her smart phone.

Jefferson had his desk-phone to his ear and nodded a greeting at Jerry. He placed his hand over the mouthpiece. "It's about your dad..." Jefferson put the phone back to his ear as Jerry's stomach began churning.

"Yeah," Jefferson said, "yeah... well, hold on..." Jefferson put his hand on the mouthpiece again. "He's okay. But they found him lying on the ground in front of your place. He'd been there for a couple hours..." He extended the handset.

Jerry's face was red as he placed the phone to his ear. Someone, a woman, was still speaking into the other end. "I didn't see the son around..."

"It's me," said Jerry, "the son. Who is this?"

"Oh! I'm Dolores. I live up the road. I used your driveway to turn around. Sorry. But that was a good thing, I guess, because I saw your father lying on his back near the garage."

"Is he okay?" said Jerry, concern overcoming his embarrassment.

"Yeah, he's okay. We're inside now. I made us some iced tea. He didn't break anything, but he says he couldn't get back up, and nobody was around to help him."

Guilt and anger rose in Jerry's gut like the head on a too-quickly-poured beer. "Where was his walker?"

"Inside the house. He said he felt like he didn't need it today. Here... he wants to talk to you."

Dad's scratchy voice came on the line. "I was gonna take some things out to the garage and save you some work."

"Well," said Jerry slowly, knowing he could never say what he wanted to say, namely that his father was more work and trouble than he thought he could endure anymore, and that he was nearing the breaking point, physically and emotionally. "Are you okay now?" was all he could manage. He felt physically beaten, exhausted. "Do you want me to come home?"

Before Dad could answer Jefferson was waving at Jerry to get his attention.

"Wait a minute, Dad." Jerry put his hand over the mouthpiece.

"Go home," said Jefferson, "you can make your time up tomorrow."

Jerry nodded, but he didn't want to go. He was missing too much time, perhaps jeopardizing his job. He took his hand off the mouthpiece. "Okay, Dad. I'm coming home. Don't go anywhere, just relax. And don't walk her to her car."

After Dad's last fall, Jerry had almost a month of quiet and normalcy, and his natural optimism began to slowly rise again like the sap that was now pushing his tired old orchard trees to bud. Jerry drove up the driveway, parked and went into the house. He paused just inside. The lamp, TV and table, and his bicycle, all lay in a jumbled heap on the living room floor. He grew angry as he realized what had happened. Dad's electric wheelchair must have snagged the cord of the lamp, pulling the table and everything on it over on top of the bike. Jerry picked up the bike. It was his only extravagance. He'd paid almost a thousand dollars for it. His anger rose when he saw that the front wheel was warped, as if Dad's electric wheelchair had been run into it or over it.

Dad's bedroom door opened and his chair whirred as he rolled out and down the hall dressed in a pair of plaid shorts and a white T-shirt. "I was trying to get in there to look for one of my CDs, but it was too tight, and I knocked your bike over. Sorry."

Jerry kept his face a blank. "I would have moved things around for you when I got home... if you would have waited."

Dad just looked at him.

"Did you know the front wheel is damaged?"

Dad squinted as he looked down at the bike. "It's only bent a little. You can still ride it."

"Yeah... at little better than a crawl." Jerry felt his pulse rise. "Damn it, Dad, this is how I get my exercise. My knees are too beat to jog anymore."

"Knees? Don't tell me about knees when I'm in this Goddamned wheelchair!" Dad's white eyebrows arched into half-ovals.

"Why couldn't you just wait for me to get back and help you, like we agreed? Now I'm gonna have to spend money I don't have to get this thing fixed!" Jerry watched Dad's bony chest rise and fall.

"At least it can be fixed," his father said, "not like my Rockwell."

Jerry's face contracted in consternation. "What are you talking about?"

"My signed Norman Rockwell print. When you were just a little squirt, barely out of diapers, I bought a Rockwell print. Cost me quite a few bucks back then. I'd framed it myself and had it sitting on my bed. I was getting ready to hang it when I had to go to the bathroom. I only left the room for a minute, but when I came back you had already marked it up with a pen and ruined it!"

Jerry was red-faced. "I don't remember that."

"Of course you don't because your mother was around to save you! But if she weren't, I'da given you a spanking you never would've forgotten." Dad turned his chair around and rolled back into his room. The door closed.

Jerry sat in the La-Z-Boy in front of the darkened TV. A shot of Jim Beam sat on the tray table beside him. Outside in the dark, the crickets and frogs droned out a cacophonous symphony. Jerry thought about going to bed. He had to get in early to make up for the time he'd missed the week before taking Dad to the dermatologist for his rashes. He took a sip of the whiskey.

Just sit, part of him thought. What's the point? His life was completely screwed up. What difference was another hour of sleep going to make? He needed three, four more. Hell, he needed a whole day…

He took another sip of the whiskey. "Don't worry about it," he said aloud to himself, "you can sleep in on Sunday."

Jerry's eyes swept the room slowly and fixed on Lisa's slippers. She'd forgotten them, and a framed picture of her son in his football jersey. He thought of calling her. No… let her go. At least someone had broken free from this.

He turned and looked down the hall at Dad's door. Earlier, Dad had called goodnight as he used his walker to get from the bathroom to his bedroom. He had only grunted in reply, no longer angry, but too emotionally drained to respond politely. He should have gone in and said goodnight properly. He decided that he would, but just not yet.

Jerry looked back over at the bike, its derailleur and gears gleaming in the lamplight. He got out of the recliner and went over and knelt beside it. Lifting the front end, he was amazed and smitten anew by how lightweight it was. What a marvel of engineering! He spun the wheel and it went around almost silently on its precision bearings, but with a slight wobble like a planet in a warped orbit. This machine—carbon fiber, chromium steel, plastic, wire, paint, and hours of engineering know how—offered him a primitive, almost sensual escape from his tedious work-a-day existence. He had loved to pedal the country blacktop for thirty, forty minutes, his pulse strong and sure, the wind in his face. Always afterward he felt rejuvenated, ready to do battle again. But now—

Outside, the ambient scratchy grinding of the crickets and frogs paused as if they'd heard or sensed something and grew afraid. A heartbeat later they started back in again.

Jerry lowered the bike back onto the floor. He got up and sat back in the recliner. A memory came to him. He used to meet Dad at the bus stop every day-something a little five- or six- year-old boy could safely do in Barlowe, Tennessee

156

back in 1966. Dad always had a little treat for him, a package of vending machine cookies or a chocolate cupcake. Dad would tell him that he'd bought them for his own lunch but had been too busy to eat them. He would then devour them happily as they walked back to the house together. He'd never thought about it before, but of course Dad had bought them just for him. So why did he tell him that story? He shrugged.

He looked over at Dad's door. Light still seeped out from beneath it. He decided to go in and say goodnight to him. He pushed out of the recliner and went to the door, opening it. Dad lay on the bed with his face to the wall. The covers were off. Without touching him, Jerry knew that he was gone. His bald head shone in the light, his short wiry white hair covering the back of his head down his neck like moss on a tree. His smooth, hairless, wooden-looking legs jutted out of his stripped blue and white pajamas, giving him the look of an over-sized Muppet.

Jerry's breath escaped in a deep, shuddering sigh. He pulled the covers over Dad, up to his shoulders. He turned out the light and closed the door. A dark mass seemed to hover over him. Its hold over him would not be denied. He knew it, but he could hold it off for a little while. He went back to the living room and knelt beside the bike. Taking out the tool kit. Slowly, carefully, he removed the front wheel. Maybe he could true it up. He grabbed the spoke wrench. It was worth a try.

- **Paul Clayton**

Long Time in the Wake

Matter is an imaginary
and exploded substance.

--David Hume

Four little girls in an exploding church
        in Birmingham in September of 1963
were always already debris.

Already viscera and brains freed of sentience,
        already the fact of red-spattered print dresses
and young aspirations freed of bodies as if,
        by some decree,
girlish life, placid Sundays, and choir practice
        no longer made the picture complete.

As if, with dispatch, in past tense, in the philosophical realm,
        glass, cinder, wood, brick, and girlflesh
had already imagined themselves in roaring pieces
        paused still flying along the alley to City Hall.

As if one could then stop-time the bang and come to see
        incendiary substance as instructive,
suspended in the crisp cool morning air
        and illustrating immutable laws.

- **Randy Blythe**

The Crossing

Inez leaned on a weathered fence post and squinted at the position of the sun. She stripped off her stained leather gloves and sipped cold breakfast coffee from a cup she had set on the top of the post hours ago. A ladybug crawled on the cup's rim and she let it crawl on down to her finger until it flew away. There was just enough daylight left to ride the filly before feeding stock and making supper. It was mid-spring and there was much to do, but Inez wanted to take time out to work with the four-year-old. In the past months, she had schooled the young horse, practiced backing and turning, and sometimes loped a few circles in the breaking pen. The filly was green, but quiet, and Inez was getting bored with the confining pen work. Today, she desired to try the horse out on the loop trail. Inez gazed past the barn at the last of the poppies and lupine that bejeweled the San Gabriel foothills. The amber and amethyst flowers beckoned her to take a closer look.

As of late, some difficulty was connected to daily chores. Inez suffered from pixies and haints that tormented and teased her. When she woke this morning, she became aware of the pickup keys—gone two days or maybe more—under her pillow. The find was timely; she needed to take a rare trip to town. But when she tried to start the engine, the ignition key wouldn't fit. In the truck's cab, Inez smelled something nasty and saw a sack of groceries tipped on the floorboard. Brownish lettuce and green-tinged hamburger lay rotting along with a swollen carton of sour milk. She blamed the hired man but realized she hadn't seen him in months. Inez was glad. He was a gossip and liar.

Now, she went to the house to ready for the ride. But the haints had stolen her glasses and the pixies made off with one of her riding boots. After long searching, Inez spotted the toe of the missing boot under ruffled newspapers and stacks of unopened mail and—

Well then.

—the lost glasses perched on top of her head as she caught a glimpse of her disheveled self in the hall tree mirror. She struggled to pull the boots on her swollen feet, cursed old age, and the accompanying ailments. Shoving a sweat-stained Resistol over bristly silver hair, she rummaged through a pile of dirty laundry for her chinks. The leather leggings were a nuisance to buckle over her jeans, but they saved the inside of her thighs from chafing on the saddle.

Spin, the cow dog, was inert on the porch when Inez finally tromped outside. The dog stretched and yawned. The border collie, in her prime, was forever slinking up and down the pasture fence line, crouching low and intent on keeping a close watch on the cows as they grazed. Sometimes she'd burst after a calf that strayed too far from the herd, biting its heels, and making it bawl. The cows were long gone and these days, Spin napped in the sun or shade according to the weather. Now, she followed Inez to the barn and stalked a lizard skittering down the aisle.

Inez slid the filly's stall door open. The little mare turned tail, but Inez was having none of that and snapped her on the rump with the end of a lead rope. The filly hopped around, surprised. Inez slipped a halter over the horse's nose, took her out, and tied her to the hitching rail. The milk crate that served as a currycomb box was not in its usual spot.

Meandering through the cluttered barn, she spied her favorite cereal bowl with the chipped edge—licked clean most likely by Spin—discovered a bib apron with three tawny hen's eggs in the pocket, and tripped over her missing corduroy slippers peppered with tenacious foxtails.

Finally, Inez saw the milk crate harboring brushes on a low stack of hay bales. She groomed the mare's glossy sorrel coat, flipped a well-worn Navaho blanket onto her broad back, and then struggled to throw the saddle over. Inez reasoned it was more weighty than usual because of the fastened canteen and the Smith and Wesson four-inch loaded with snake-shot—holstered and rigged over the horn. When she threaded the latigo through the D-ring to tighten the cinch, the filly pinned her ears and pawed the ground. Inez took a braided horsehair bridle from the hook nearby. The handsome bridle had been a gift from her husband, Mr. Parrott, on the occasion of her sixtieth birthday some years ago. Plaited red, black, and tan with a jaunty shoofly on the cheek piece, Inez stopped to admire the intricate work.

She slipped the curb bit into the filly's mouth, pulled the crown piece over the velvet ears, and took care to smooth the trapped hairs of her forelock. She finished up by stroking the mare's silky neck.

Inez led the horse into the barnyard. She crouched down and then up to pop her arthritic knees, stretched her tight, aching back by twisting to the right and left, and stood on a little mound of dirt to gain some height to lift her stiff leg into the stirrup. Grunting and heaving, Inez was half-way mounted when the filly walked off and made Inez hop about on one foot to keep up.

The saddle pulled sideways and she just managed to get her foot out of the stirrup before she was dragged. She shoved the saddle back in place, rightened the girth and tried again.

Once onboard, Inez made adjustments to the reins and squeezed the filly into a walk. Out of habit, she waved at the house and then wistfully recollected there was no one there to see her off.

She rode down the dirt driveway, crossed Aliso Road that split her property, and up the dusty trail she had traversed on many other horses for umpteen years. Spin trotted along behind, also out of habit. It was a fine afternoon, the best part, when the sun hung low over the hill. Inez knew the path crossed the creek twice on the short loop where the dog could wade and drink. The filly had never been through the water, but it was shallow and narrow. Inez reckoned it shouldn't be a bother for the quiet, young horse.

The trail led the shuffling filly, Inez, and Spin to the south slope of the hill. Around the bend was a profusion of wildflowers and Inez caught her breath. It had been years since they'd bloomed in such abundance.

Long ago, when she and her son gathered calves for branding, Inez pointed out flowers and identified them. But now the names escaped her as did her son's whereabouts so she could ask if he remembered.

The trio was nearing the crossing. When the mare saw and heard the stream rushing over jagged rocks, she stopped and snorted. Inez urged her forward but the horse rolled her eyes, tensed, and backed up.

C'mon, Filly. It's not an ocean. Don't get muley on me.

Inez pointed the horse at the creek and gave her a kick. Impatient, Spin splashed into the shallow water and lapped at it. The mare jigged and circled. Inez was not going back home. That would be letting the horse have her way. She clicked her tongue and managed to urge the anxious horse to the edge of the bank. The mare planted her hooves and stared wild-eyed at the glittering stream. Spin, sensing it was wise to get out of potential harm's way, sloshed to the opposite side. She shook the icy water off her coat and rolled in warm sand to dry.

Beneath Inez, the filly felt like a giant, coiled spring. There was a fine line as to how much leg pressure she could apply to the horse's flanks—too much and the mare might whirl or worse, rear-up.

The filly made a decision. She rocked back, gathered under Inez, and sprang high to vault the awful water. She caught Inez unawares and when the mare left the earth, Inez left the mare. In the instant that Inez was launched straight up out of the saddle, instinct made her grab for the saddle horn. But the break was violent and she grabbed sky. The filly shot out from under her. Inez slammed to earth on her back and every bit of air squeezed from her lungs. All thought flew from her head as it cracked the ground.

Inez worked her mouth like a beached carp and wheezed until her breath came in short, raspy gulps. She lay still with her eyelids pinched shut, heard what sounded like the dial tone of a telephone, and wondered who she meant to call. Her eyes fluttered open and she saw verdant cottonwood boughs swaying above. For a moment, she thought she was waking from a little lie-down in her hammock. The buzzing in her head ceased and the pleasant gurgling of water in the creek retold the fact that she had just been thrown from the filly.

It sure wasn't the first time she'd been pitched. She knew better than to just get up. Inez took inventory. Her head hurt some but her hat was still on because it was a good fitting hat. She squinted at her feet and sure enough, there they were—with legs attached. She urged them to move. They wouldn't obey.

Inez had landed clear of the water in a patch of rock-strewn blue sage. Nearby were granite boulders that lined the creek bed and she was thankful she didn't put down there.

She felt something trickling from her right ear and touched the place with the tips of her fingers which came away bloody.

Propping on her elbows, Inez saw the filly grazing on the other side of the creek. Spin sat in the shade of a tree, panting, and watching Inez.

The filly ate her way to the edge of the water, then without hesitation,

161

walked in knee deep, and took a long drink.

Ain't that just the way.

Inez hoped the horse would come near so she could make a reach for a stirrup and pull to her feet.

The mare ambled up the bank toward Inez with the bridle reins dragging in the mud and stepped on one. She jerked her head and the aged leather snapped from the tension. Easing closer, the horse sniffed at Inez's legs. Inez extended an arm ever so slowly, then grabbed for the near stirrup. The horse shied away, stopped, and nibbled some bunch grass.

The world tilted to a crazy angle and Inez laid her head back to stop the gyratory. The last light of dusk had deepened the sky to indigo between the branches above. Sparrows roosted, twittered the news of how their day had gone, and advised where to find a safe place to settle in. She witnessed the first greenish star wink to life. As a child, she and her sisters had wished on that self-same star.

Did her yearnings come true?

Inez sensed Spin beside her and caressed the dog along her bony spine. Spin licked Inez's face and shifted closer. There was kindliness in Spin and Inez loved her for it.

Something rustled the brush out of sight and she wondered if the filly had stayed around or gone back to the barn. She knew horses weren't like they showed them to be in the movies. Her experience was that they were neither heroic nor faithful.

She decided she had lain there long enough and it was time to be getting home. There was the filly to catch before the saddle was trashed but other thoughts invaded. Inez hadn't yet watered the garden. The new tomato plants might wilt. She worried about the revolver strapped to the saddle and hoped no kid would get a hold of it. Inez knew Mr. Parrott would have chastised her for keeping the gun on the saddle instead of on her hip. She used to wear it, but as the years went by, and the pounds came on, the butt of the gun bruised her side. Inez purchased the special saddle holster with grocery money—since her husband refused to buy it for her—and now the Smith and Wesson was with the filly and not with her. She thought if she had it, she could squeeze off a shot to alert some help or if it got real bad…maybe take her out of misery.

Inez felt tears gather, then shame. She didn't hold with that sort of thing. She rested her hand on Spin's head as the night became serene and cold came upon them. Considering her situation, she wondered when was the last time she had seen anyone else on this trail? Calling on her ornery reserve, she managed to scoot backwards using the thin strength left in her arms. She removed her hat and propped her aching head on a smooth, pillow-sized rock.

She rubbed her numb legs to enliven them until the activity wore her out and she stopped, licked her cracked lips, and wished for the canteen—also strapped to the saddle.

Frogs and crickets chirped their evening melody. It was the same tune she heard from the safety of her porch. But the chorus was far purer here by the rippling water—like being in a living, breathing church.

Inez took comfort and dozed.

When she awoke, the moon glowed above. Inez gasped. She had never seen it so pallid and full. She reached out to touch it, but pulled her hand back when a white moth hovered over her head. Her mama had told her that moths were really lost souls and that's why they flitted around so. Inez felt beside her for Spin. She was gone. Inez's heart quivered.

Maybe she ran for help like a Lassie dog. Inez laughed out loud at the absurdity and the crickets and frogs went silent.

She had trouble taking a breath, braced on her elbows, and went into a fit of hacking. She coughed up blood. Shivering, Inez commanded her body to heed her desire to go home. Her own flesh was becoming separate from her will, being treacherous, and acting on its own accord.

When the sun comes up… I'll get back in order.

But the high, baleful moon told her there were hours until dawn.

It occurred to Inez she might have left a stew or some soup simmering on the stove for supper. She often did that. It would boil to a scorch and likely burn her house down. She rather liked the idea. What a worry it was as to who would take possession of the place when she was gone. Her boy had moved on. Who would work the ranch? A profound ache pressed the walls of her chest.

Exhausted, Inez turned her head to watch for the possible glow of flames over the hill. Instead, she saw Mr. Parrott sitting at ease on a fallen tree trunk. Inez knew he was dead, but she was grateful he had managed to get away from the graveyard to be with her. He was silent and seemed discomfited to find her resting on the damp creek bank in the dark. Inez sighed in resignation.

She sat up, brushed off, and got to her feet—surprised that she could. Taking him by the hand, they crossed the graceful water together, hopping from rock to rock like they did when they were kids.

They strolled to the top of the hill and studied the moonlit ranch they had worked endless hours stretching into seamless years. This was the place they loved and hated above all else. It wasn't ablaze after all. It lay tranquil and hushed. From this height it seemed in much better order than when Inez left it earlier. Perhaps Mr. Parrott had fixed it up while she was out for her ride on the filly. Even if he had, Inez knew the ranch would be everlasting needy and the tasks of upkeep were now pointless.

Inez made a decision. She turned to her impassive husband.

I was happy here.

Mr. Parrott nodded.

Satisfied, Inez gathered the remaining spark of herself. She rocked back like the filly had and sprang high to leap free from the insatiable land.

- Kat Fandino

163

The First Time

I remember the first time it happened. The sun was shining and the spring air was refreshing. I was invincible. I climbed up the stairs, and gazed up into the sky. The clouds mesmerized me as I watched them slowly merge and take on different shapes.

Suddenly, I was struck with a blow and the wind got knocked out of me. Not physically, but with the power of words. *"NO GIRLS ALLOWED. We were here first!"*

The group of boys were shouting at me. I glared at them and continued climbing. I had every right to be here, just as much as they did. It was imperative for me to reach the top so I could be closer to the clouds.

One of the boys stepped on my foot and I let out a yelp. He looked at me and laughed. The other boy tried to block me from entering the next level to get to the slide. Again, I had to finish my mission so I asked him to please move. They laughed at me, but I made my way up level and onto the giant slide. It was worth it to get to the top. I reached my hands towards the sky and almost touched the clouds. It was magical.

Then it happened again. Over and over, every time I tried to climb up the ladder or the ropes or the steps. I was tired of asking them to please move so I decided to quit using the word please and just say it directly. They still didn't move. I ducked under one of their arms and moved quickly to the top. I was spritely and it helped me ascend quickly. I stood at the top in front of the slide and heard them say, "You're just a dumb girl." I slid down the slide while I let the tears slide down my cheeks.

Running to my grandmother, I buried my face in her shoulder. I wanted to be strong, but those words hurt. Then I heard something that forever changed me. A woman walked up to the boys and loudly questioned, "Did I just hear someone say that girls are dumb? Listen! I don't want to hear that again. Girls aren't dumb. Boys aren't dumb. Be kind!"

She was only a head taller than the boys, but had a surprisingly loud voice. I instantly liked her. I got the vibe that she was trying to calm down as she walks up to me. Kindly, she asked how I was and she told me a story about how sometimes it is okay to be brave and push forward. Other times, she said it is best to remove oneself from a situation. It takes learning what you need to stay true to you, but told me something powerful. *You get to decide. They don't have that power. Don't ever release it to them. You have it and you can either keep plowing through bravely or bravely know when it is time to move along. Either way, you are brave! Always stay true to yourself.*

- **Jessica N. Arzola-Grissom**

Four Thousand Dollars

two
pencil scratching
paunchy guys
came out
to bid the job
They got paid

then

two
little ladies
with mops
and buckets
came out
to do the work

- **Elizabeth Harmatys Park**

Contributors

Jessica N. Arzola-Grissom resides in a small Texas town with her husband and son. She loves traveling, reading, chocolate and tea. In her spare time, she writes and records a podcast titled "The More You Know".

Gustavo Melo (he/him) is a Brazilian satirical writer with a successful track record of one failed marriage by the age of 25. Knowing little about smart financial decisions he got a highly practical master's degree in writing for screen and television at the University of Southern California. To deal with those and other failures he often writes humorous pieces which he workshops by testing whether his therapist will finally throw in the towel.

Rachel R. Baum is the editor of *Funeral and Memorial Service Readings Poems and Tributes* (McFarland, 1999) and author of the blog Bark: Confessions of a Dog Trainer. Her poems have appeared in *Poetica Review, New York Quarterly, East Ridge Review, New Verse News, Raven's Perch, OneArt,* and others. She chaired the committee that selected the first Poet Laureate of Saratoga Springs.

Art Bell is a former television executive. His short stories have been published in *Castabout Literature* (July 2019) and *Fiction Southeast* (2021). His memoir, *"Constant Comedy: How I Started Comedy Central and Lost My Sense of Humor,"* was published in September 2020 by Ulysses Press (Berkeley, CA). Art currently lives in Park City, Utah where he hikes, skis, and plays piano and drums.

Randy Blythe lives in north Alabama. His poems have appeared in a number of journals, among them *Portland Review, Aji, Tar River Poetry, Chicago Quarterly Review,* and *Pleaides.* "Long Time in the Wake'" appears in his 2023 full-length collection, The Wish Furnace, and is published here courtesy of FutureCycle Press.

Kasey Butcher Santana is co-owner/operator of Sol Homestead, an alpaca farm. Recently, her work has appeared in *Geez Magazine, The Hopper,* and *Farmer-ish.*

Thomas Cannon is the inaugural Poet Laureate of Oshkosh, WI. His books include *Shattered* and *The Tao of Apathy.* He has poems and short stories in *Mid-western Gothic, Corvus Review,* and others.

Patti Cassidy has been a freelance writer, playwright, photographer and documentary maker and is now devoting her time to writing memoir in scenes.

Melanie Chartoff is a stage, screen, voice actor, new author, and recently published in *McSweeney's, the New York Times, Isele Journal, Entropy, Crows Feet, The Jewish Journal, Funny Times,* and five editions of *Chicken Soup for the Soul*

Fred Cheney lives in the rural Maine house where he grew up.

Paul Clayton has been writing fiction all his life. His 'fictionalized memoir,' *Carl Melcher Goes to Vietnam,* was a finalist at the 2001 Frankfurt eBook Awards along with works by Joyce Carol Oates, David McCullough, Amitav Ghosh, and Alan Furst.

Douglas Cole published six poetry collections and the novel The White Field, winner of the American Fiction Award. In addition to the American Fiction Award, he was awarded the Leslie Hunt Memorial prize in poetry, the Editors' Choice Award for fiction by *RiverSedge,* and has been nominated three time for a Pushcart and seven times for Best of the Net. He lives and teaches in Seattle, Washington.

Matt Daly is the author of the poetry collection, *Between Here and Home* (Unsolicited Press), and the chapbook, *Red State* (Seven Kitchens Press). Matt is the co-founder of Write to Thrive, an enterprise that brings reflective and creative writing practices to individuals and professional groups to cultivate creativity and wellbeing.

Shaheen Dil was born in Dhaka, Bangladesh, and lives in Pittsburgh, Pennsylvania. Her poems have been published in over two dozen literary journals and anthologies. She has new work forthcoming in *CALYX Journal, the Atlanta Review, Uppagus* and *Critique of the Gods.* Her poem, "River at Night" won Honorable Mention in the Passager 2021 Poetry Contest. Her first full-length poetry collection, *Acts of Deference,* was published in 2016 by Fakel Publishing House in Sofia, Bulgaria.

Roxanne Doty's debut novel, *Out Stealing Water,* was a finalist in the Autumn House 2019 fiction contest and was published by Regal House Press, August 30. 2022. Her short story, *Turbulence,* (Ocotillo Review) was nominated for the 2019 Pushcart prize for short fiction. Other stories and poems have appeared in *Superstition Review, Forge, 170 Review, Soundings Review, Four Chambers Literary Magazine, Lascaux Review, Lunaris Review, Journal of Microliterature, NewVerseNews, Saranac Review, Gateway Review* and *Reunion-The Dallas Review.*

Mario Duarte is a Mexican American writer and an Iowa Writers' Workshop alumnus. His poems and short stories have appeared in *Native Skin, Many Nice*

Donkeys, New Croton Review. New work is forthcoming in *iō* Literary Journal, and *Mannequinhaus,* and a short story collection "Monkeys" is scheduled for release in 2024.

Robert Earle's short fiction has appeared in more than 100 literary journals, including *Consequence, The Literary Review, Eclectica, Seattle Star, The Common, Black and White, Steel Toe Review,* and many others. He lives in Durham, North Carolina.

Kat Fandino studied creative writing at UCLA and screenwriting classes with Christopher Lockhart, story editor with William Morris Endeavor. She has written for regional papers and has a romantic comedy screenplay optioned.

D. Marie Fitzgerald is a retired English and creative writing instructor. She is also the author of four books: Reruns, A Perfect World, I Have Pictured Myself for Years, and F&G. She resides in Palm Springs, California where she runs a poetry critique group and a monthly authors series at which she presents two local authors. Her work has appeared, most recently, in *Cholla Needles, Academy of the Heart and Mind, The Northern Indiana Review,* and *Plainsongs.*

Casey Ford is director of the Lamar University Writing Center in Beaumont, Texas, where she teaches first-year composition and creative writing. She earned an MFA from Fairfield University. Her poems have been published in *Amarillo Review, Concho River Review,* and *Last Stanza Poetry Journal,* the latter of which honored her with a 2023 Pushcart Prize nomination.

Lisa Friedlander is a psychotherapist and essayist. She likes to quilt together ideas, sensory details, experiences and stories that sometimes mesh, sometimes conflict or cause friction. Her work has recently appeared in *Pink Panther, First Line, The Forge, Lavender Bones, Shark Reef, Ponder Review, Wild Roof* and others.

Joan Gauscheman is a mother, elementary school teacher, dirt worshipping word crafter who lives in the desert south of Santa Fe, New Mexico. *Un mensaje de los apus* was written while in Crestone, Colorado as a way to honor the teachings of the naturaleza which help her keep perspective and stay grounded when overwhelmed with grief at the state of our modern world.

Anyély Gómez-Dickerson knows the pain of assimilation in a home not my own. She's a teacher of twenty-three years, with experience in creative writing and poetry at the college level. She aims to empower marginalized voices suffering inequality and injustice; those often misrepresented or appropriated by the mainstream. She's a Cuban author whose work will appear in NALAC's literary journal this spring.

Mary Grimm has had two books published, Left to Themselves (novel) and Stealing Time (story collection), and a number of flash pieces in places like *Helen, The Citron Review,* and *Tiferet.* Currently, she is working on a YA thriller.

Danielle Guthrie writes both poetry and prose ranging from visceral comedies to dark fantasies. Beyond writing, Danielle has worked as an editor for *The Bolo Tie Anthology* and YEGWrites Press. Originally from Vancouver Island, she now resides in Edmonton, Alberta. She is currently working on her first novel.

Susan Hettinger, a Wyoming native and former attorney, lives and works in Olympia, Washington. She's a 2022 Pushcart nominee and a finalist in the 2022 Tobias Wolff Award for Fiction. Her stories have appeared in *Cagibi, The Madison Review, New World Writings, Fiction Factory, Scribble, Please See Me, Washington Law & Politics* and *Seattle Magazine.* She has studied creative writing at Hugo House, the University of Washington, and Bread Loaf Writers Conference. She's now an MFA student at Oregon State University.

C. L. Hoang was born and raised in Vietnam during the war and came to the United States in the 1970's. He graduated from Ohio University and the University of California, Berkeley and earned his living as an engineer, until bitten by the writing bug a few years back. He has since published a novel, a travelogue, and a collection of stories. His writing has also appeared or is forthcoming in *The Threepenny Review, Consequence, The Louisville Review,* and *Louisiana Literature Journal,* among other publications.

Emma Jarman is an emerging creative writer enjoying short fiction and memoir. She is an Ohio native and recovering journalist, currently working in special education at a small public school in Oklahoma. She is chronically dehydrated and has almost always lost her Chapstick.

Milton Jordan lives with Anne in Georgetown, Texas. Now and then she forwards a poem to a friend. More rarely friends send a comment on the poem. Milton co-edited the anthology *"Lone Star Poetry,"* for Kallisto Gaia Press.

Carella Keil is a writer and digital artist who splits her time between the ethereal world of dreams, and Toronto, Canada, depending on the weather. Her work has appeared recently or is forthcoming in *Columbia Journal, Skyie Magazine, the cover of Glassworks 26, Wrongdoing Magazine, Deep Overstock, Nightingale & Sparrow, Existere, Superlative Literary Journal, Stripes Literary Magazine, Writ-*

eresque, *Chestnut Review, Door is a Jar, Sunday Mornings at the River, Grub Street* and *MONO*.

Carrie Kornacki is a veteran English Language Arts teacher, with years of teaching in the U.S. and in China. She teaches Creative Writing for Writers in the Schools/Houston, coordinating and launching youth chapbook projects. In 2015 and 2016, She was the recipient of "The Lucille Johnson Clark Memorial Award" awarded to the top Houston Poetry Fest juried poet who teaches public school.

Nathan Alling Long grew up in rural Appalachia, worked for several years on a queer commune in Tennessee, and now lives in Philadelphia. Their work appears on NPR and in various journals, including *Tin House, Master's Review, Electric Lit,* and *Witness.* The Origin of Doubt, their collection of fifty short fictions, was a 2019 Lambda Award finalist.

Rachael Magruder is a student at University of Louisville studying creative writing and women's studies. She lives in Louisville, KY with her husband and cats. "How to Grow a Baby" is her first published piece.

Joe Manion is an emerging writer of literary and speculative fiction living in Northern Virginia. He helps run a nonprofit for disabled adults and occasionally seeks inspiration on motorcycle trips to the Blue Ridge Mountains. His most recent fiction appears in *Spank the Carp* literary magazine, and *Dark Recesses.*

Tracy Mayo has two degrees from Duke University. After a homesteading experiment she embarked on a career in commercial construction management, as a trailblazing woman in a man's world. Her writing has appeared at Aspen Summer Words juried workshops, and in *Heimat Review.* She lives in Boulder.

Nell McCabe received her MA in English with a concentration in creative writing fiction from the University of Missouri–Columbia in 2010, and currently teaches creative writing, literature, and composition at Berkshire Community College in Western Massachusetts.

Benjamin Nash currently has *Sun* available at Finishing Line Press. He has had poems published in *Concho River Review, Louisiana Literature, Pembroke Magazine, 2River,* and other publications.

Deborah Oluniran-Adeniyi writes from Nigeria. None of her words have appeared online.

John Palen's latest book, *Riding With the Diaspora,* won the 2021 Sheila-Na-Gig chapbook competition. Recent work has appeared in *Sleet, Willawaw Journal, Cider Press Review,* and *Book of Matches.* He lives on the Illinois Grand Prairie.

Elizabeth Harmatys Park PhD received the First Place Jade Ring Poetry Prize awarded by the Wisconsin Writers Association and the New Feathers 2020 Award. She is the Racine, WI Poet Laureate for '23 and '24. Her poetry is published in journals and in anthologies such as *Bards Against Hunger, Ariel, From the Ashes, Poetry for Ukraine* and *The Milwaukee Anthology.* She writes with Authors Echo in Burlington, WI and is a regular contributor to the Wisconsin Poets' Calendar. Elizabeth has published three chapbooks: "The Sun Exists to Love the Earth", "Traces", and "Theater of Seasons".

Janet M. Powers, Professor Emerita at Gettysburg College, has published poetry in many small journals. Her chapbook, Difficult to Subdue as the Wind, appeared in 2009.

Tiffany Promise (she/her) is a writer, poet, chronic migraineur, and the mother of two wildlings. She holds an MFA from CalArts, and her work has appeared in *Narrative Magazine, Brevity, Creative Nonfiction, Okay Donkey, Jarnal,* the inaugural issue of Francesca Lia Block's new literary magazine, *Lit Angels,* and elsewhere. Tiffany lives in Austin, Texas.

Nicole Pyles is a writer living in Portland, Oregon. When she's not hunting down the right word, she's talking to God, reviewing books on her writing blog, watching movies, hanging out with family, and daydreaming. Her work has been featured in *Ripley's Believe it or Not, WOW! Women on Writing, The Voices Project, Sky Island Journal,* and *Arlington Literary Journal.*

Nora Raleigh has fifteen published novels for young adults. Many of these books have won awards including the 2010 American Library Association Schneider Family Book Award for *Anything But Typical* (S&S), and in 2016, an International Literacy Association Notable Books for a Global Society for *Ruby on the Outside* (S&S).

Candice Rankin was the chapbook prize winner in *Wingless Dreamer, East/ West Journal,* and *Typehouse Literary Magazine.* Candice is a memoirist at heart and shares stories of humor and trauma about the rural midwest and her dysfunctional family.

James Roseman received his MFA in Creative Writing and Literature from the Bennington Writing Seminars. His work has been published in *3 Moon, Clover & White,* and *Sage Cigarettes.*

Sara Rosenberg holds a master's in Writing and Publishing from Emerson Col-lege and has published poems in *Pine Row Press* and *Borderlands: Texas Poetry Review*. She also writes and edits grant proposals for a nonprofit focused on edu-cational equity. She lives in Austin, Texas.

Jim Ross jumped into creative pursuits in 2015 after rewarding research career. With a graduate degree from Howard University, in eight years he's published nonfiction, fiction, poetry, photography, plays, hybrid, and interviews in nearly 200 journals on five continents. He recently wrote/acted in a one-act play and ap-peared in a documentary limited series broadcast internationally. Jim and family split their time between city and mountains.

Shana Ross is a recent transplant to Edmonton, Alberta and Treaty Six Territo-ry. Qui transtulit sustinet. Her work has recently appeared in *Cutbank Literary Journal, Laurel Review, Phantom Kangaroo, Barren Magazine* and more. She is winner of the 2022 Anne C. Barnhill prize and the 2021 Bacopa Literary Review Poetry competition, as well as a 2019 MVICW Parent-Writer. She serves as an editor for *Luna Station Quarterly* and a critic for *Pencilhouse.*

Mervyn Seivwright writes to balance social consciousness & poetry craft for hu-mane growth. He is a nomad from a Jamaican family, born in London,England, and left for America at age 10, now residing in Schopp-Germany. Mervyn com-pleted a writing MFA at Spalding University and has appeared in *AGNI, Amer-ican Journal of Poetry, Salamander Magazine, African American Review,* and 55 other journals across 6 countries.

Trisha Tavares is a Caribbean pediatrician who lives in Arizona with her husband and one son. She has been writing since childhood.

A.J. Terlesky is a Canadian/Ukrainian writer who currently resides in Atlanta, Georgia where they are finishing an MFA in Creative Writing. A.J. Terlesky's fo-cus in on flash fiction and poetry.

Marissa Tian is an Asian first-generation immigrant living in Houston, TX and non-native English speaker who works full time as a commodity trader for an investment bank and writes in her free time for passion. One of her stories won the Stories That Need to Be Told 2022 contest, another was a finalist for the 2022 Tobias Wolff Award for Fiction in the *Bellingham Review.*

John Thomson lives in Penn Valley California.

Daniel Tierney is a Vietnam vet who has published stories both online and in print. Several stories have been shortlisted for prizes. He published a book of short stories and a war memoir. He lives in NYC.

Korey Wallace's poetry has appeared in *The Briar Cliff Review, Helix, and From Whispers To Roars*. His poem "Leftovers" won the Musepaper prize. He is in Paramedic school and works as an EMT in Sioux City, IA.

Sarah Weglarz is a writer of mainly poetry but also dabbles in fiction and short story. She loves to read horror novels and the otherworldly and weird. Sarah is from Westchester County, New York. Her work has been published in the *Raven Review*. She enjoys exploring the darkness of abandoned places, the late neon of motel signs and the ocean in autumn.

Louise Wilford lives and works in Yorkshire, UK. Her work has been published, in *805, Last Leaves, New Verse News, Pine Cone Review, Punk Noir, River and South, Silver Blade, The Avenue, POTB, Balloons Lit, Parakeet, The Fieldstone Review,* and was nominated for Best Of The Net in 2022. In 2020, she won First Prize in the Arts Quarterly Short Story Competition, and was awarded a Masters in Creative Writing (Distinction). She is working on a fantasy novel.

Printed in the USA
CPSIA information can be obtained
at www.ICGtesting.com
BVHW042007300723
667991BV00005B/20

9 781952 224348